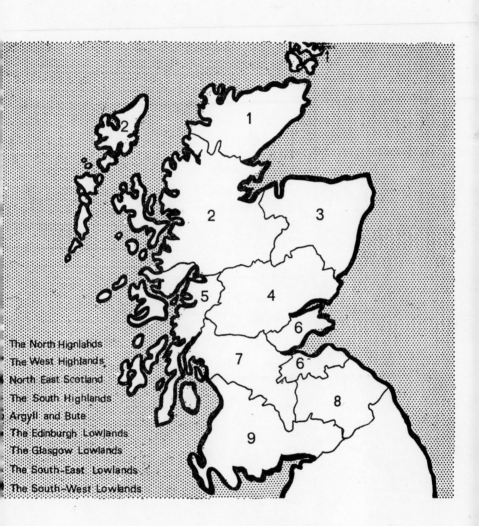

The North Highlands
The West Highlands
North East Scotland
The South Highlands
Argyll and Bute
The Edinburgh Lowlands
The Glasgow Lowlands
The South-East Lowlands
The South-West Lowlands

FARMING IN SCOTLAND

THE FARMING IN GREAT BRITAIN SERIES

Edited by ROSCOE HOWELLS

Preface by
Rt Hon. The Lord Netherthorpe, LL.D., B.Sc.

Farming in Scotland

by

ROBERT URQUHART

DR

DAVID RENDEL LIMITED
138 NEW BOND STREET
LONDON, W1

PRINTED IN GREAT BRITAIN
BY W & J MACKAY & CO LTD, CHATHAM

CONTENTS

PREFACE

BY THE RT HON.

THE LORD NETHERTHORPE, LL.D., B.SC.

THE inspiration for this series of books entitled 'Farming in Britain' sprang from an original work by Roscoe Howells, who wrote the first of them, *Farming in Wales*—making it the prelude to a new pattern of agricultural presentation.

That was indeed a brave adventure, for many had previously failed in the discharge of this task which Mr Howells has so successfully accomplished.

Many phrases have been used to describe farming. Here is but a selection: 'A way of life'—'Not a way of life, but a business' —'A struggle with natural hazards'—'The harnessing of the productive potential of an indigenous natural resource, the land'— 'A means to an end'—'A wealth-creating industrial enterprise' —'A reservoir of the human qualities of tenacity, veracity, optimism, and simple faith'—'A life in the happy and romantic environs of the countryside with the disciplines of country lore'.

One could, I suppose, list many more and each might of itself provide the basic theme for a treatise on farming, but in the process each would tend to constrict the scope of its readership.

There never was any magic in making the complex more complex; real art lies in making the complex simple. There is no human endeavour more complex than farming, despite its apparently simple objective. Yet the interplay of the forces it creates, of the forces it has to face or of the forces with which it becomes involved, has so far-reaching an impact on society as to merit a better understanding by the greatest possible number of people.

To supply such understanding is the fundamental aim of this most commendable series.

Knowledge is the prerequisite of understanding, and it is

wise to seek to understand before you blame. Blame for the shortcomings of the farmer is so often based on a failure to understand. The task of explanation could be approached from a variety of angles. For example, a romantic rural novel might hold its readers, but lose force through the author's licence in moulding fact to fiction. An economic analysis could be so dry as to dry up its potential readership. The story too simply told might seem merely patronizing to some readers, and might still puzzle others.

What a challenge it is then to an author to write informatively whilst not overwhelming us with details, to be objective without pontificating, to dwell on the humanities without sentimentality, to be vivid without parochialism, to be assertive without being aggressive, to sustain interest without romanticizing.

This wellnigh impossible task has been successfully carried out in this series, and it speaks highly for the worthy gentlemen who have written the volumes from the respective regions. All are men with a sound knowledge of farming in general, and of farming in their own area in particular.

The series, therefore, is a remarkable contribution to public knowledge. It goes a long way towards meeting the real need—that is, of enabling the greatest number, regardless of age, to gain a new insight into the realities of farming and of the British countryside.

The rapidity with which the agricultural industry has advanced through the application of new technologies over the last quarter of a century is also remarkable, and the magnitude of its contribution to the national well-being is irrefutable.

An appreciation of the purposes of agriculture, its achievements, and its problems is an urgent national need. These publications edited by Roscoe Howells are a bold and worthy contribution to the mutual understanding that is required of townsman and of countryman alike.

CHAPTER I

FARMING ALL OVER THE WORLD

I T was nature which gave our countryside its physical appearance or outline. Movements of the Earth's crust or volcanoes threw up the rocks and mountains, and great rivers or glaciers gouged out the valleys or brought the soil down to create great flat areas. Later the rocks 'weathered' over the centuries and created more soil.

So while Nature gave the countryside this basic appearance, it was man who provided it with its 'complexion'. It was man who drained the bogs and created green fields, who replaced many of the natural forests of old and clothed the hillsides with what the Norwegians have called 'green gold', for, as in many countries, the forests there are measures of national wealth. It was man who built the roads and the cities and the towns and put his stock to graze on the upland areas which were too difficult to cultivate. In fact, many books could be written about the impact of man and animals on our countryside.

It was, of course, a long and gradual process, faster in some countries than in others, as man progressed from primitive or nomadic types of civilization, from the days when he made himself a crude weapon to kill an animal for food, or followed the crops or pastures with his little herds or flocks in the days before he realized the possibilities of cultivating these crops.

It was when man stopped depending on naturally grown food and started cultivating the ground that he became a farmer, when he stopped living on the growing fruits or berries or roots he found in their natural state.

While farming has developed in different ways in different parts of the world, it has one thing in common and this is that all farmers are largely dependent on the weather—although, as we shall show later on, some farmers in some countries have made efforts to make themselves less dependent on climatic conditions. But, by and large, it is still true that farmers do depend on the physical conditions in which they work. The most important of these physical conditions is the weather, but they also include the types of soil, the temperature of the countryside in which he lives—and this will be governed largely by its latitude, or distance from or nearness to the Equator—and also the elevation and aspect of his farmlands. By elevation we mean whether it is high on a hill, which will add to the problems, and by aspect we mean whether it faces north or south, or where it lies in relation to the prevailing winds.

Just as we all know what a difference the weather can make to the enjoyment or otherwise of a holiday, so we can also realize what a difference it can make to the success or otherwise of the different farming enterprises, but we shall see that some are much more dependent on the weather than others.

Weather conditions can bring a farming enterprise to a highly successful conclusion or result in disaster.

In those very early days all the men who produced food did not produce the same kinds of food. Some got it by hunting animals and some by searching for the fruits and berries and other types of growing food. As there was no such thing as money in those days, people producing different kinds of food would use barter or exchange one type of food for another. This would apply to the people who started making weapons for the hunter, or for defence, or clothes, and gradually a system built up whereby the farmers or food producers could provide their other needs by first exchanging food for them and, later, tokens or money.

Alongside the hunter and the other food producers and the people who made clothes and utensils and weapons there were those who cured animal skins, for clothing or adornment. All the time the process went on which we call improving the standard of living. This was a continual process which is still going on today although, of course, over the centuries, it received severe setbacks through devastation by war or flood or pestilence.

But it still goes on and today it is the farmer who is one of the key forces in this process of improving the standard of living of the peoples of the world. Today it is the agriculturally progressive and highly productive countries which are helping with the food and surpluses to raise the standard of living of the less fortunate, or, as we call them, the still developing countries.

Again we must come back to the important consideration of the conditions in which the food producers or farmers operated. These conditions, and climate, remember, is one of the most vital, dictated what type of crops were grown or what kind of animals or what breeds of animals were reared and bred. As communities got larger, that is communities where the people who lived in them were not directly engaged in food production, this flow of food from the countryside and the flow back of goods or cash in exchange developed.

It follows from this that the wealthier these communities were the better was the market for the products of the countryside around them, or even for products from much farther afield, for really wealthy communities could import foods or delicacies from distant countries as civilization developed and did not depend only on the produce of their own hinterland.

So, in addition to climate and soil and other conditions, the size or wealth of the population to be fed had its impact on the farming which served it. Population and soil have a bigger impact in some countries than others. For instance, in China, with its teeming millions, the farmers grew crops which suited the soil and were cheapest. So in many countries of the East, because of this huge demand for the minimum food to maintain life, rice is the staple food, for the land could not be spared for the production of meat—or, perhaps more important, the food producers there did not have the technique, the equipment, or what we sometimes call 'the know-how' to produce anything but those cheap foods.

It is, in fact, today a sign of the rising standard of living in many of these developing countries that as they improve their national wealth more of their people wish to eat meat rather than cereals. This is not easy in some of these new countries, because they do not [have the minerals on which to build industrial wealth, or perhaps the know-how, or even good enough soil for increasing their agricultural wealth. But scientists,

engineers and administrators, and people from such organizations as the Food and Agricultural Organization of the United
Nations, are all doing their best to try to even out at least some
of these serious handicaps which so many countries have in
feeding themselves let alone in getting enough food for export.

These are just a few of the things we must understand before
we begin to understand properly the farming activities which
are going on around us. What we do know from this problem of
the conditions imposed by the climate is that there is no point
in us trying to grow certain exotic fruits in Britain any more
than there is any point in expecting countries with a hot climate
and little grass to breed and rear cattle for beef or milk, or sheep
for mutton and lamb. Many people in Britain like rice, bananas
and oranges, and so on, but we get them from the countries
where they grow easily and therefore more cheaply.

So there we have it—climate and poverty or wealth have
their effect on markets, or on supply and demand for the
farmer's products, which, it must be remembered, include
many items of clothing as well as of food. So while farmers have
the common problems of climate to contend with—varying as
they do in different parts of the world—they also have the
common objective of helping to feed and clothe their fellow-
men.

In Britain we produce what the climate permits us to produce, what the market requires and what it is profitable to
produce. The fact that Britain is a relatively small segment of
the countries of the world does not mean that it has not very
wide variations in its farming, for even in a small country like
Britain the pattern varies quite considerably and it all makes for
a great deal of interest. It is very doubtful, in fact, if such a
remarkable variety of farming types or systems in such a small
area of land could be found anywhere else in the world.

Scotland is a country where there are wide variations of all
the conditions we have mentioned—climate, aspect, elevation,
and soil condition, different in many ways from other parts of
the United Kingdom. There are obvious reasons why some areas
should be devoted to hill cattle or sheep, or to lowland sheep,
or to milk or to cereals or potatoes and so on.

There is one aspect of Scottish farming which many people may not realize. Like the other countries which make up the United Kingdom of Great Britain and Northern Ireland, Scotland is a very great and famous industrial country, famous for its engineering, shipbuilding, and similar enterprises, for its place in the newer science-based industries of electronics and industrial chemicals, and for many years noted all over the world for its fine tweeds and woven fabrics. But in spite of the wealth and activity these impressive industries create in Scotland, by far the biggest single industry in Scotland is agriculture, with a total value of produce sold off Scottish farms of about £200,000,000 a year. And the other point about Scottish farming is that about 80 per cent of Scottish farmers' incomes are earned from livestock or livestock products, so Scottish farming is based on livestock or the products from livestock that is—beef, mutton, pork, bacon, milk, butter, or cheese, eggs, and poultry meat.

And behind all the operations which produce these are well-thought-out plans which ensure that the industry will not only cope with the present needs of the country but with those of the future.

In this book we shall be trying to achieve a better understanding of these things, and to outline what Scottish farming is and what it does.

CHAPTER 2

THE AREAS OF SCOTLAND

ONE of the things which surprises, and often impresses, overseas visitors to Scotland is the remarkable variety of farming conditions in the country. This variation arises from the amazing differences between different areas. It would be easy to say that the main division so far as farming goes in Scotland is that we have the Highlands and the Lowlands, but that would be oversimplifying the situation.

One of the first things you will notice about Scotland from the map is that apart from the rather short Border with England, the country is not only surrounded by sea, but has off its northern and western coasts a very large number of islands which are divided into three main divisions—the Northern Isles, which comprise Orkney and Shetland; the Outer Hebrides, which include Lewis, known as the Long Island, and its 'tail' of other smaller but still important islands stretching southwards; and finally the Inner Hebrides, which include Skye, Mull, Islay, and other islands of the west.

These three island divisions have their own types of farming, and even in the two sets of Northern Isles there are differences to be found. There is a saying that the main difference between the crofter, or small farmer, of Shetland and of Orkney is that in Shetland he is a fisherman who has a croft while in Orkney he is a crofter who has a boat, indicating that many of the people living on the land there have a link with the seas, but with the emphasis rather different between the Orkneys and the Shetlands.

While Shetland farming is in the main extensive farming, that is sheep and cattle kept on moorlands or small areas of grass—with, of course, a number of farms of the more normal type—Orkney is a county where the islands have much more cultivated land. Orkney's farming intensity has earned it the name of 'Little Denmark', for it has a great reputation for hard-working small farmers who have won a name for themselves in the production of good beef cattle, eggs, milk, and pigs, although there have been years when distance from the market and other handicaps have proved difficult for some of the farmers engaged in particular enterprises. But Orkney is really famed for the high quality of its beef stock, mainly the hardy black cattle breed from the Aberdeen-Angus or Shorthorn, of which we shall hear later.

Orkney has also an interest in dairying and produces a cheese which has won a market on the mainland and far south.

A lot of land has been reclaimed from the heather in Orkney and is now well-cultivated farmland, and this is still being added to; but, because so much has been done there, there is little scope for much more. In islands like the Shetlands and Lewis the scope for reclaiming the heath for farming is much greater, and these islands have in more recent times brought great credit to the farmers and crofters there for their work in reclaiming or improving poor land and so making any given area of land not only carry more stock but carry the heavier types of stock.

Coming round to the west and farther south to the Inner Hebrides, we have another huge assortment of islands, some of them quite big, islands like Mull and Islay, which, by the way, are also very mountainous in parts. In the more fertile areas of many of these islands good arable land is found, so that more feed can be grown for the stock—but this problem of feeding the sheep and cattle through the winter is perhaps the biggest single problem in Highland and island farming. For instance, hay which may be selling at £8 per ton in the carselands of Stirlingshire, where much of it is grown, could cost twice that or much more by the time it is transported by road or rail and then shipped to, say, the Isle of Mull.

Since 'The Highlands and Islands' are often linked in one phrase, we will look at the rest of the Highlands, and here there is more subdivision. There are the Central Highlands which, as their name implies, lie in great ranges of hills in the middle of Scotland, ranges like the Grampians and the Cairngorms. The Cairngorms are the highest range of hills in Britain with several lochs lying at heights above the height of Snowdon, which is the highest mountain south of the Border.

The Western Highlands are different hills again, ranges running westward to the sea, with in many cases long sea lochs running far into them.

A special feature of the Western Highlands and islands is that their climate is much milder than might be expected. This is because the Gulf Stream, after its journey across the Atlantic carrying warmer water and warmer air with it, practically touches the coast at some points.

It will be easy to understand that all these different factors— the islands with little high ground, the mountainous islands, and the Central and Western Highlands, not forgetting the effect of the proximity of the Gulf Stream—have resulted in special patterns of farming in these areas.

There is another distinctive area of Scotland where the farming can be called hill farming, although the hills do not reach the heights of the mountains of the Central and Western Highlands. They are called the Southern Uplands, and they cover an impressively large area of the south of Scotland, the Border hills, the Cheviots and the smaller ranges a little to the north, the Moorfoots, the Lammermoors, and the Pentlands, with, to the west, some higher and more heathery hills. A feature of the Border hills is that many of them are green right over the tops and so make good sheep country.

These hills and uplands form a very large proportion of the land area of Scotland. In fact, about two-thirds of the land— outside that covered by towns and 'industrial uses'—is classified as 'rough grazings'.

The richest farmlands of Scotland are in places like the Lothians and counties like Berwickshire, in Fife and the lower parts of Perthshire, and the rich counties—farmingwise—like Angus with its fertile Vale of Strathmore, and the north-east corner and Moray Firth coastal areas, where between the sea and the lower foothills there are areas of rich farmlands noted for their productivity and quality of produce.

We must not generalize that the rich farmlands are confined to the coastal plains, for there is one other feature of Scottish

Plate 1 *Farmers often co-operate in trials and experiments. On this farm in Angus, the trial was on different applications of fertilizers on barley. The differences are very evident. (Photo S.A.I. Ltd.)*

Plate 2 *Stockfeeding is a highly mechanized business. The twin towers on the left on this Border farm hold silage while the single tower on the right holds barley. The silage and barley are mechanically extracted from the towers and fed through augers to cattle in large courts on the other side of the buildings.*

Plate 3 *Spreading basic clag on a farm near Biggar in Lanarkshire. (Photo S.A.I. Ltd.)*

geography as it affects the country's farming and that is that
there are many long river valleys which broaden out into
areas called straths where the land is also good, with deep soil.
Two examples are the long valley of the Spey, which runs
north-east to the Moray Firth from the heart of Inverness-shire,
and Strathearn in Perthshire, another broad strath in its lower
reaches. One farming writer called the Spey 'The Valley of
the Champions', for if we take the Spey and its tributary rivers
and near-by areas, no region of its size has provided more
champions at the great Royal Smithfield Show in London.
There are others such as the Dee and Don in Aberdeenshire.
There is a saying there:

'The Dee for fish and tree
'The Don for horn and corn.'

The inference is that the valley of the Don is more noted for
its farming—stock and cereals—while the Dee is more famous
for its scenery and its salmon fishing. But while upper Deeside,
where the Royal Family enjoy long late summer and autumn
holidays at Balmoral, does earn its tribute, there are also some
good farmlands in the lower reaches of the Dee.

Inverness-shire, Scotland's biggest county, which stretches
far west to include the big Isle of Skye, is among the most
Highland of the Highland counties, but it, too, has good farmlands around the Inner Moray Firth, and in the border area
with Ross and Cromarty there are rich pockets of farmlands
such as the Black Isle, which is not an isle at all but a broad
peninsula lying between two firths.

So we have mentioned the islands, the Highlands, the rich
farming areas of the coastal plains, and the more fertile examples
of some of the broad straths and river valleys. Which leaves the
south-west, another area with its special contribution to Scottish
farming.

The main interest in the south-western counties is dairying,
which is natural in an area where there is high enough rainfall
to maintain good green grass.

But we must not think of these areas as separate compart-
ments, each producing its own speciality, for there is dairying,

as we have mentioned, in Orkney as well as in other areas of Scotland, and there are 'pockets' of contrasting types of farming inside areas which may have their own regional pattern.

So far as meat is concerned, and by this we mean chiefly beef and mutton and lamb, we could look on the hill, upland and island farms as taken together, forming a great reservoir from which comes the raw material for our beef, mutton, and lamb. Many of these upland farms are breeding or rearing farms for the stock which are taken down to the Lowlands and fattened there, because the hills have not the food resources to fatten the store stock as the animals to be fattened are known.

CHAPTER 3

CLIMATE AND GROWTH

BEFORE we consider the ways in which climate affects and influences our farming it would be just as well if we first of all considered exactly what we mean when we speak of climate. Very simply it means average weather conditions, but if we look in the dictionary we will see that climate is referred to as 'the condition of a region of the Earth's surface as regards temperature and atmospheric changes in their relation to, or effects upon, plants and animals'.

In the chapter just before this one we remarked that much of Scotland is surrounded by the sea, the Atlantic Ocean and the North Sea. During the long summer days the sea becomes warm and retains some of the heat during the winter months. In just the same way if we take a boiling kettle off the fire it does not get cold straight away. It takes time to cool off and the more water there is in the kettle the longer it takes to cool. A vast area of water like the seas which surround Scotland takes a long time to cool, and during the autumn and winter, when this cooling off process is still taking place, the sea has the effect of keeping the land warmer than it would otherwise be. Obviously this is more noticeable near the coast than it is farther inland, and this effect would be less marked in central Scotland.

During the summer when the hot weather comes the sea is still warming up after being cold in the winter and this has the effect of keeping the land cooler than it would otherwise be, and, of course, the effect gets less the farther we go inland.

This results in the coastal areas having what we call a more equable climate, with less variation from very cold to very hot, than the areas farther inland.

One of the reasons for this is that there is this steady drift of warm surface water in the Atlantic in an easterly direction—the Gulf Stream. So a westerly wind will bring warmer air to the areas nearest the flow of the Gulf Stream, while to the north of the influence of the stream the conditions will be relatively colder.

The Gulf Stream has a surprisingly marked effect on certain parts of the West of Scotland, where at one or two points it is possible to see palm trees growing in the open, thanks to the generally moist and relatively warmer air. Some years ago, in fact, an internationally known fibres company was investigating the possibility of growing 50,000 acres of bamboo in western Scotland with a view to producing cellulose. This might not be the tall bamboo you think of in certain really warm countries, but bamboo of a certain variety could be grown, and, in fact, some patches of it can be seen here and there. The scheme fell through because there was not nearly sufficient acreage available to provide what was needed to keep a factory in full operation.

In the south-western areas of Scotland, in some very favoured patches of the countryside where the conditions are dry and sufficiently frost free, early potatoes can be planted and they are really early potatoes.

But these western areas where the warm moist Gulf Stream air comes in also have a high rainfall, as the warm air stream comes in and hits the hills or meets colder air and condenses to form clouds or rain.

So these warm moist winds which sweep over Scotland from the west bring a heavy rainfall to the western coasts and the mountain slopes ranging from 40 to as high as 120 inches a year, depending on the height. This is far higher than the east coast regions, where some areas away from these rain-bearing winds have annual rainfalls between 20 and 30 inches.

These climatic factors in the west have their effect on the ground there, creating in many areas boggy conditions, and these in turn have their impact not only on the type of farming but even on the stock. Later we will be mentioning the breeds of cattle. The shaggy Highland cattle of the Western Isles and Highlands have long shaggy coats, not so much for the purpose of keeping out the cold as for getting the rain to drain off them.

Another effect of this condensation in the mountain areas is the fact that there is often low cloud and mist at times when the lowlands will be enjoying sunshine. So it is that the higher we go not only do we get more rain but less sunshine. This means, in turn, that there is less sunshine to evaporate or dry out the moisture in the land which has been created by these conditions, and the ground in many places in such areas is soggy, with bogland being quite common.

The natural growth in these areas will depend to some extent on whether the ground has become bogland in this way or remained drier where the natural drainage of the soil has been more effective.

Where the land is drier the natural vegetation is coarse grass, bracken, and heather. Lower down trees grow more easily until we get down to the coast itself. Here growth is subjected to the force of the strong westerly and south-westerly or northerly winds blowing during the winter. These are laden with salt from the sea which 'burns' some of the growth and, where there are trees or bushes at all, they seem to have developed their growth only on the leeward side, which is the side away from the one exposed to these fierce winds. Even then they will be very stunted in their growth.

The effects of these winds from the sea or off the land, even in the spring or summer, may be quite damaging. In the very dry area of the farmlands of East Lothian, a strong, drying wind off the land has been known to remove much of the dry topsoil, and with it the seedlings of, say, turnips, and blow them all into the sea, and away to the north in Orkney or some similar area a high wind from the sea, carrying salty spume with it, can cause severe damage to or even complete loss of a cereal crop.

These, then, are the natural things which are happening all the time and which have such a great influence on the farming in different areas. These conditions cannot be altered. Man therefore has to accept them and adapt his farming methods so that the conditions interfere as little as possible with his activities and, wherever he can do so, use them to his own advantage.

Grass is a crop which needs moist conditions and rain from time to time. There are therefore, considerable areas of Scotland, especially in the south-west and in some other regions, where conditions are good for growing grass and not so good for growing corn.

And there are very large areas of Scotland where it is difficult to grow corn. There are millions of acres of 'uplands' where there are rough grazings on which hardy cattle and sheep can be reared. They produce the calves and the lambs which are fattened on the better lands of the lowlands. And there are other areas where, owing to the rather moist conditions, it is easier to grow grass than corn and they, too, are predominantly livestock areas where the farmers feed the grass to their livestock and produce livestock products such as milk, beef, and lamb.

It will be seen from a map of the British Isles that there are parts of England and Wales which are similarly situated to Scotland and where the same conditions will, therefore, apply. Indeed, because of this factor of climate and grass growing potential, the whole of the western seaboard is predominantly a livestock area. Thus it follows that, generally speaking, the up- lands and the moister areas of the west and south west, along with the Highlands, are the main livestock areas of Scotland.

Even so, there are certain variations within the overall pat- tern and other areas also traditionally produce livestock. These include Orkney and large parts of the north-east such as Aberdeenshire and Angus. There is also a great tradition of livestock rearing, fattening, and breeding integrated with the predominant pattern of cereal production in some of the quite dry lowland areas.

Thus it can be appreciated that, although Scotland is dif- ferent from some parts of England, there are other parts which, because of this question of climate, have farming problems similar to our own and their farming pattern is very much like that which is found in Scotland.

When we understand these things we are in a better position to appreciate why farmers do certain things. We often hear townsmen ask why a farmer does not take a certain course of action, or grow a certain crop, or why he goes on keeping cows when it is no longer profitable to produce milk. Why doesn't he grow corn instead? We have seen enough in these early chapters to know that many of the farmers in certain areas cannot grow corn because of the climate, or at least they cannot grow it as a major crop for sale—as a cash crop—but where they grow it at all, it is for feeding to the stock as a supplement to the grass or the natural herbage of the hillsides.

These farmers are more or less restricted to livestock farming, and if they have spent money on cowsheds of dairy equipment, as many in the south-west have done, it is not always as easy as it may seem to turn to some other form of livestock farming.

Then, there is the question of market requirements and finances. These are just as important to farmers elsewhere as they are to farmers in Scotland, and they present common problems. Milk, for example goes from the milk-producing areas to the big cities, so that in many respects there is an interdependence between farmers in different areas.

But unlike the effects of situation and climate, these other considerations are of man's creation. As such they are more variable. They change from time to time and are sometimes more difficult to understand.

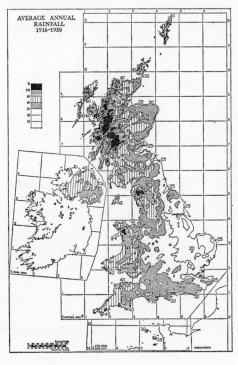

AVERAGE ANNUAL
RAINFALL
1916–1950

CHAPTER 4

FINANCE AND PRICE FIXING

IT will be recalled from the first chapter that finance has an important bearing on the way in which the farmer conducts his business. Men no longer barter with each other for their simple requirements. Money has been introduced and our way of life is far more complicated than it was in those far-off days. In the present structure it would be out of the question for each farmer to barter with someone else for each item which he produces or which he requires for the running of his business. Most of the bargaining, therefore, has to be done with a group of men acting on behalf of their fellows.

In various regions or districts farmers meet to discuss their problems. It is also important for them to know what farmers in other parts of the country are thinking about and to get their support in the many things they are trying to achieve. But, of course, it would not be possible for all the farmers in one district to meet all the farmers in another district. So at each district meeting the farmers elect a number of their fellows to speak for them at meetings with elected representatives from all the other districts of the county or region, which may include more than one county.

These county or regional meetings are held at regular intervals in a central place where it is most convenient for delegates to gather. Afterwards the delegates can report back to their fellow farmers in their own districts about what has transpired.

It is not sufficient for farmers in each region or county to discuss their problems in this way. In turn they need to meet farmers from other counties, and to this end each county or area meeting elects one or more representatives—depending on the size of the area—who can meet representatives of other counties on a national basis. Every area in Scotland thus keeps in touch and in direct contact with farmers in other areas. This organization is called the National Farmers' Union of Scotland and is generally referred to as the N.F.U. Not every farmer in Scotland is a member of the N.F.U., but a very high proportion are, and in some areas nearly 100 per cent of the farmers are members, with a total of about 24,000 in Scotland as a whole.

So it is easy to understand that the N.F.U. is the body accepted as the organization which speaks for the farmers of Scotland. And it is the leading members of the N.F.U. who every year bargain on behalf of their fellow farmers with the representatives of the people who wish to buy food produced by the farmers. This annual negotiation on prices is known as the February Price Review, because it is held about this time of year. The results of the negotiations are usually announced about that time, although negotiations go on for many weeks before the final announcement.

The same thing applies, of course, in the case of the interests of those, the consumers, who buy the farmers' produce. The farmers' leaders negotiate with the Government as being the elected representatives of the people. Obviously it would be impractical and unnecessary for every member of the Government to be immediately concerned with such negotiations, and the work is therefore delegated to the Ministers responsible for dealing with agriculture in Britain.

There is the Minister of Agriculture, who looks after agricultural problems in England and Wales. Scotland has its Secretary of State, whose job includes the administration of agriculture in Scotland, so far as the Government is concerned. He works in co-operation with the Minister in England at price review times, when the leaders of the Scottish N.F.U. meet in London for the review along with the union leaders representing England and Wales and Northern Ireland.

At this annual Price Review it is the task of the farmers' representatives from the three United Kingdom Farmers' Unions to produce facts and figures to prove how much it costs to produce certain commodities and to show how the price should not fall below a certain figure in order that the farmer shall be able to obtain a fair return for his labour and the cash he has invested in his farming enterprise.

The Ministers have people to advise them who say whether they think the figures produced by the farmers are correct. It is the Ministers' duty to ensure that there is sufficient food of good quality for the people to eat at a price which they think they can afford to pay. When these talks have been concluded the Ministers report to Parliament on what has taken place and on what has been decided. The result is generally announced in Parliament by the Minister of Agriculture, who speaks on behalf of the administration of agriculture in all three regions of the United Kingdom, but if there are any questions, say on points of interest to Scottish farmers, then they are answered by the Secretary of State for Scotland, who is Scotland's 'Minister of Agriculture'.

Possibly the members of the Opposition will criticize the recommendations, but usually the Government will support the Minister, and his decision will, therefore, have a most important effect on farmers' affairs.

The farmers do not always agree with the decision taken by the Minister. Whether they agree or not, however, it is he who has the last word and this leads, in the event of the farmers' leaders not agreeing, to what is known as an 'imposed settlement'.

In trying to be fair to both sides the Government has two important considerations to bear in mind. The consumers for their part require a plentiful supply of food at reasonable prices. Some of this comes from foreign countries which, in turn, buy the products of our factories, and it is an argument involving high economics as to how far we are justified in believing that it is sound business to take agricultural produce from them in return for our manufactured goods to an extent which can be detrimental to the interests of our own farmers. Whilst farmers recognize that trade with other countries is essential to the economy, they also have every right to demand a fair share of the home market.

What is even more important, perhaps, is the fact that it is in the interests of consumers that our own farming should be prosperous. For one thing, farmers themselves buy a large amount of the things which are made in our factories and they also do a great deal of business with tradespeople in the towns. They can only do this if they have the money to spend.

The other most important consideration, of course, is the fact that we cannot always be sure that we can buy food from abroad. If war breaks out, for example, it is imperative that we produce all the food we can at home. If there is a political crisis or civil war in some distant part of the world we may suddenly find that we cannot buy something we need very much. Perhaps it will be sugar from Cuba or beef from the Argentine.

At such times we are very glad to know that we have sugar-beet crops in East Anglia, and also in some parts of eastern Scotland, and beef cattle on our own farms, so that we would not have to do without these commodities completely. If we left a motor-car in the garage for a few years without going near it we would not expect it to start up without considerable attention. If we wanted to get away on urgent business we would then be very sorry that we had not been sensible enough to ensure that the engine was in good running order.

It is the same with our farming. We must at all times ensure that it is in good running order to be ready in case it is urgently needed.

If we neglected our agriculture and then suddenly were forced to produce as much food as is possible in an emergency, it would take time for land to be reclaimed and crops to be planted and harvested. Where could we suddenly find enough cows to produce the milk we needed or the beef or the sheep? For that matter where would we suddenly find the people with the knowledge to do the job? It is also a fact that if we have a reasonable supply of anything already assured, there is no need for us to pay a very high price for the extra we require. Other countries know this and they are therefore unable to take advantage of us as they would be able to do if we were entirely dependent on them for all our needs.

There is also another important point. The population of the world is increasing rapidly and there is no knowing what demands there will be for food in the next few decades. At the same time we are losing a large amount of land every year in this country for housing, factories, schools, hospitals, and roads. So that it becomes even more important that we should produce as much food as possible from the land which remains. As we have seen, the farmer can only continue to do this as long as it is profitable for him to do so.

These things must all be balanced one against the other by the Government when it is considering how much the farmers will be paid for what they produce. The Government must also take into account that when we buy from abroad it costs us money. What we produce at home, therefore, can save money for the nation. The Minister has to decide what can be bought most cheaply and what it is in the nation's interest for our own farmers to produce in order to bring about the greatest saving. This may vary from time to time according to world affairs, so that the profitability of certain things we produce at home will also vary according to what the Minister thinks the consumer should pay and according to what demand there is. That is one of the variable effects created by man.

It is also necessary that there should be an understanding as to how much of any commodity we require. The Minister may well say the farmer should be paid a certain price for producing up to this amount, but if he produces more than this, then the price will be less, so that the farmers' leaders will try to ensure that this standard quantity is sufficient. It is what we have already referred to as demanding a fair share of the market.

If it is thought to be in the national interest for consumers to be able to buy certain of their food requirements at less than what it has cost to produce them the Minister may decide to introduce a subsidy. Although the farmer receives the subsidy, it is paid on behalf of the consumers for their benefit. These subsidies are paid in different ways, but the purpose is always the same, either to keep down the cost of the food to the consumer or to ensure a plentiful supply at a reasonable price.

Sometimes this is done by paying farmers part of the cost of putting up new buildings or fences, for draining the land or putting lime on it. The consumers still derive great benefit from these payments, because they enable the farmers to keep more stock and produce more livestock products more cheaply than if they had to bear the whole cost themselves. Obviously if the farmers had to pay for it all themselves they would expect more money from the consumers for their produce.

The money to pay for these subsidies and grants comes out of the money collected from the whole country, both consumers and farmers, in taxes. When it is used in this way it is being used for the benefit of everybody and it is the duty of the Minister to ensure as far as possible that the money is used wisely and fairly.

Perhaps we can better appreciate the importance of all this if we remember that farming is Britain's biggest industry, the total output of which is double the value of the output of either our coal-mining or motor industries.

It is greater than the total agricultural production of Australia and New Zealand put together. Farming is not only the biggest industry, it is also a very efficient industry. For every man employed in British farming we produce enough food for twenty-three townspeople. This is more than any other country in Europe. In Denmark a farm worker feeds seventeen townspeople, in Germany nine, in France eight, whilst in Italy the figure is as low as one to seven.

Lastly, it is important for us to remember that when the Minister is negotiating with the farmers' leaders in this way he is negotiating on behalf of the consumers of the whole of the United Kingdom, and is therefore very much concerned with the overall picture. We in Scotland are concerned with how things affect us and we can understand this much better if we understand the whole story. Our immediate concern for reasons which we have already seen is mainly with the price of livestock products.

Our chief interest in arable farming is, for the most part, only in so far as it fits in with our pattern of livestock farming. On the other hand, if the corn growers in other areas are doing well we know that they are less likely to turn to milk production and compete with farmers in the livestock areas who cannot grow so much corn. We want these corn growers to do well so that they will be able to pay the best possible price for the cattle they buy from the stockbreeding and rearing areas. They also grow much of the corn and hay which is used as feedingstuffs bought by the livestock farmers of the western areas. Always there is this interdependence between farmers in different areas and the conexion between many things in the general pattern.

There is not only interdependence. There is a kind of built-in 'opposition' between some sections. For instance, it is estimated that for every cereal grower who wants as high a price as possible for his cereals there are four livestock farmers who want cereals at the cheapest possible price to feed to their livestock. The system of guaranteed prices already described helps to reduce this apparent opposition in that the grower gets a guaranteed price which is above the price actually paid by the stockfeeder. Again this helps to keep the cost of production of livestock products down.

Now that we have examined some of the factors which affect farming in general and farming in Scotland in particular we should be in a better position to take a closer look at what is happening in the countryside with a view to obtaining a more complete understanding.

CHAPTER 5

THE GENERAL PATTERN

T HERE are one or two paradoxes about farming in Britain and one has already been brought out in the preceding pages. It is that while we are brought up, quite rightly, in what we are taught in school and what we read in the daily Press, to believe that Britain is a great industrial and manufacturing country, it is nevertheless a fact that the biggest single industry is farming, which is bigger, in value, than almost any other two of our big manufacturing industries combined.

Another paradox is that many townspeople think of farming as an industry where the men in it, the farmers, do not go in for violent, revolutionary changes, but plod along the road of progress. This is just not true. When we take an interest in what is going on in the countryside around us we become aware that things are constantly changing and changing very quickly. There have been changes ever since time began, and this is what we know as evolution. Nowadays, however, things are changing more rapidly than they have ever done before, and this rate of change is perhaps one other factor to be borne in mind because of the important effect it has, in conjunction with the other factors we have already considered, on the way in which the farmer sets about trying to earn a living from his land.

New machines are being invented. The design of existing machines is being improved. Always it is man's aim to use machines as much as possible, both to make life easier for himself and his workers and to save the money paid in wages to those who do any job which is not as yet done by machine.

Chemists and scientists are constantly introducing new sprays which the farmer can use to control weeds. There are now selective weed-killers which will kill certain weeds, but which will not affect the crop in which these weeds grow.

Then there is the invention of new drugs for the prevention

of disease in livestock. Their use has made it possible to keep larger numbers of animals than ever before, and this is a good thing, because of the tremendous increase in the world's population which is now taking place.

Perhaps this vast increase can be compared with the old catch question about the water lily. A water lily starts to grow in the centre of a circular pond. It doubles in size every day and in six months it has covered half the pond. How long will it take to cover the remainder of the pond? The answer is, of course, one more day. Yet, although we are told it doubles its size every day, how surprised we are to realize that the remainder of the pond can be covered so quickly compared with the time it took to cover the first half of the pond.

When we think of the millions of people in the world and the probable increase in the population in the near future we realize what people mean when they speak of the 'explosion' in the world's population. When we realize this we also realize how difficult it would be for the farmers of the world to provide enough food for everybody and how essential it is for farmers to make use of all the new inventions and techniques which are constantly being made available to them. It has taken thousands of years for the world's population to reach its present figure, and the advancement of agriculture has kept pace with the increase. Now that we are faced with this 'explosion', as we call it, methods of food production will have to advance very quickly for enough food to be produced for everybody. Consequently the rate of change becomes very great and no sooner does the farmer get used to one idea than he has to change it for another one. New ideas and techniques can very quickly become old-fashioned and what may be good common sense today could be old-fashioned and outdated in a few years' time.

Exactly what changes will take place with our livestock in the years ahead it would be difficult to say. Over the years in Scotland, as in other areas, a definite pattern has developed. Whatever developments take place would need to be built on the pattern we already know.

In the hilly areas of Scotland, for example, we see sheep dotted about the slopes and on the rough land. These hardy animals

Plate 4 *Filling with fertilizer a combine drill which will sew oats and fertilizer along with them at one operation.* (*Photo S.A.I. Ltd.*)

Plate 5 *A fine study of Clydesdales ploughing up a field at Hatton of Cargill, Perthshire.* (*Photo Cowper, Perth.*)

Plate 6 *Haycocks in the sun. (Photo S.A.I. Ltd.)*

Plate 7 *A binder going round a field between Stirling and Perth. Note stooked sheaves in background. (Photo S.A.I. Ltd.)*

Plate 8 *Harvesting at Arrat Farm near Brechin where the horses are still to the fore. (Photo Couper, Perth.)*

are sure-footed creatures well able to look after themselves and
to look for their food in such areas, where it is in short supply.
Very often the farmers who keep these sheep actually live and
have some land in the area around the 1,000 feet-level. This
poor land and any low ground of poor quality is known as
marginal land, but with the sheep and cattle from these marginal
areas there is a strong link with farming in the lowland and more
fertile areas.

We shall be dealing with the breeds of sheep and cattle in
detail later, but it is interesting to look at this interaction between
the lowlands and the hills in this great and varied pattern of
breeding, rearing, and fattening which provide us with so much
high-quality meat in the shape of beef and lamb and mutton.

The hardy cattle and sheep which range the hills can seldom
get enough food for them to be fattened off and sold for meat,
but they can exist there and maintain themselves in a healthy
state in winter and summer and produce lambs and calves.
This is where the interesting pattern begins to emerge. Take the
the sheep, for example.

The Scottish Blackface is a small, hardy hill breed and, inci-
dentally, the most numerous sheep breed in Britain. It is to be
found, for instance, in areas like Dartmoor, where its hardiness
and ability to keep itself on the moor or hills all winter is appreciated. Naturally its lambs are small, but they produce excellent
meat. In the main, however, the ewe lambs are retained in
sufficient quantities to provide replacements for the hill flocks,
while the male lambs are sent down the hill to be fattened and
slaughtered as wethers, the name for castrated male sheep.

Some farmers can, of course, fatten these hill lambs off themselves. Some of the female lambs are mated with a heavier
breed on lower ground, so that their offspring produce a greater
weight of meat and can be fattened on the lower ground. We
shall detail this in the chapter on sheep breeds. So you can see
that these breeds on their own or mated with other heavier
breeds on lower ground provide a way of using all the ground
from the high hills, through the poor marginal lands to the
fertile areas, all for producing mutton and lamb.

It should be made clear that while the Blackface's main job

is to produce females for replacement and for crossing with heavier breeds, the Blackface lamb itself is a delicacy very much in demand in the big meat markets of the south, like the Smithfield market in London.

This is called the 'stratification' of the sheep industry, from the high hills down to the lowlands, and a similar pattern can be followed in cattle, which we will refer to when we come to the breeds.

In the hill farms of Wales a similar pattern of sheep breeding can be found in the production of the Welsh Halfbred, which come down from the hills for the production of lambs for fattening. In other words the light mountain breed is crossed with a heavier breed to produce bigger lambs which will make more use of the better grazing on the lower and richer farmlands.

As we have said, there is a similar pattern with beef cattle. As with sheep, few of the hill or other marginal lands could provide enough feed to fatten the cattle on them, but, like the sheep, these hardy hill cattle can maintain themselves on the hills and provide the herds which breed calves to be brought down the hills for fattening or crossing, and to produce stock which will make better use of the better grasslands low down. To put it another way, the hills may be looked upon as the 'reservoir' of the raw material from which we get a valuable quantity of good meat, and it shows how important these hill areas are to the lowlands in providing them with stock for fattening, just as the lowlands are of value to the hills in providing the market for their lambs and calves.

It is worth mentioning that after several years spent on the hills producing their yearly crop of lambs the old ewes are not quite finished. When they get older and their teeth begin to wear and it is more difficult for them to maintain themselves on the rough grazings, many of these ewes are bought by lowland farmers because the ewes are capable of grazing the better pastures. So these cast ewes, as they are called, may produce another crop or two of lambs after their spell on the hills or poor marginal lands, like the land on some of the islands.

One of the controlling factors in hill farming, as we have mentioned, is the quality of the soil, and a great deal of effort is expended in trying to improve its quality, so helping the farmer to improve his output from the same area of ground. Therefore a lot of land reclamation or land improvement is going on in many of these marginal land areas all the time. We have already mentioned the payment of subsidies or grants for liming, fencing, and drainage. There are also grants for plough-ing up these difficult areas. Now we can understand why these grants are necessary and the way in which they help the town dwellers by providing this source of good food—and, inci-dentally, helping to offset the great loss of land around cities for housing, roads and so on. It is important to the nation that the hill areas should be constantly supplying animals for the lowland farmers to fatten. These animals sold for fattening are known as store stock, store lambs, or store cattle. Not very long ago an important committee set up by the Government to look at Britain's natural resources made a special point in its report about the vital importance to the nation of using *all* its natural land resources and not allowing these poorer, marginal lands to degenerate into uselessness so far as food production is concerned.

From what we have been saying about the loss of so much good land in the lowlands for what is generally termed urban development, plus the fast-expanding world population, it should be clear that the development of the hills and similar areas for food production will be even more important in the future than it is now.

We have also seen sufficient of the factors which influence farming to recognize that if farmers are to be expected to farm in the hills, where farming methods are bound to be restricted, then it must be possible for them to make a profit. Without the benefit of these grants they would have to be paid more money for what they sell, which can only be store lambs or cattle, so that the meat in the shops would be much dearer than it is now.

One of the problems facing the farmer in the hills, where the rainfall is so heavy, is that the water which soaks through the land is constantly dissolving and carrying away many of the materials on which the grasses feed. These important elements are 'leached' away. Possibly the most important of these is the lime, which is essential to keep the soil fertile and sweet. It is therefore necessary for the soil to be constantly replenished with adequate supplies of lime. Another point is that bracken will flourish on land which is deficient in lime and this is not only a troublesome weed to the farmer but one which is costly to eradicate. Much of the reclamation of hill land to which we have already made reference has involved the ploughing up of bracken, often on steep ground where it is difficult to use machinery. Scientists have also been at work on chemicals to deal with this bracken problem and have met with considerable success.

It is from the marginal areas that the animals go up to the higher land to graze in the summer and down to the lower land to be fattened. In the olden days in Scotland, herdsmen walked up to the hills with the animals and often stayed with them in rough buildings known as sheilings.

In the old days before farmers had the benefit of mechanized transport they had to walk their stock to the nearest mart, so it was necessary for these marketing centres to be within reasonable distances of the farms, often not more than ten to fifteen miles apart. Many of these centres were for the sales of stock from the upland farms. In the lowland areas, however, there would be centres which would include dairy stock, cattle for producing milk, and butter and cheese.

With the coming of mechanical transport, first the railways and then the road transport, the pattern of marketing and, with it, production changed. It was easy to transport stock and products over longer distances more quickly. Milk is an example. Formerly many areas produced milk for local needs, but with improved transport and means of collecting milk, areas which produced milk more easily than other areas—owing to the better supply of good grass—could produce milk to be transported to the bigger centres of consumption.

Before the 1930s the marketing of milk was in a very unsatisfactory state, but early in the 1930s milk marketing boards were set up and the position improved greatly. We shall be looking at this development in marketing later on.

The changes brought about by these developments, land improvement and marketing improvement, were reflected in the events of the countryside such as the county or agricultural shows. Those shows in the hill areas were dominated by the hill breeds of sheep and cattle and in the milk-producing areas by dairy cattle, or in the other areas by dairy and beef cattle and several breeds of sheep. The shows and breeds we will discuss in following chapters.

CHAPTER 6

WINTER AND HOUSING PROBLEMS

IF the average townsman were to be asked what was meant by 'harvest', it is more than likely that he would think of fields of grain in autumn being cut by the machines which have replaced the sickles of olden days. But harvests are many in farming. There is the daily harvest which sees the milk appear regularly on the doorstep, just as regularly as the bacon and eggs appear on the breakfast tables of the millions who still prefer this typically British breakfast.

From all these and many more harvests the farmers gather the produce which provides millions of people with their daily food, and now that we are going to look at some of the more important factors of farming in more detail we should be able to see how plans are made to achieve the overall harvest of home-produced food in Britain. We do not produce all our food from our own fields, only some foodstuffs in which, to use the normal term, we are 'self-sufficient'. The main commodities in which we are self-sufficient, or nearly so, are liquid milk, eggs, and potatoes. We have to import a lot of our beef and lamb and bacon and also cereals for making bread. There are some foodstuffs where the degree of self-sufficiency is affected by factors other than those which limit home production, such as lack of acreage, the right climate, or soil conditions. An example is bacon. Because some overseas countries, like Denmark, are very big buyers of our manufactures, these countries get an agreed share of the British market for some of the foodstuffs they produce. Denmark is a big customer for our industrial goods, so she gets a fixed share of the bacon market. This is done by international agreements and these agreements cover a number of commodities and foodstuffs. Some of these agreements are not exactly welcomed by our home farmers, who feel that they should be allowed to grow more food for our people, but it is

obvious that with this big business in international trade some
kind of understanding with overseas countries is necessary. This
is especially so with the countries of the British Commonwealth,
most of whom get 'preference' on our market. For instance, we
have agreements with New Zealand and Australia on the supply
of mutton and lamb, and the huge imports of New Zealand
lamb naturally have a bearing on the numbers of lambs our own
farmers produce.

It was perhaps well to have pointed out these other factors
before beginning to look at some of the important features of
Scottish farming in more detail. Because Scotland is just that
much farther north and has such a high proportion of hill or
rather poor lands, the farming pattern over a large area of the
ground is affected by these factors, and especially in winter-
time.

All farmers need to plan their operations, whether they are
hill sheep men or farmers with big lowland farms producing a
variety of things, ranging from potatoes and fat sheep to cereals
and sugar-beet. These farm plans or records will give details of
the rotation of the crops round the fields, details of the fertilizers applied to these fields, or the yields per acre of different
fields of different crops, or the stock-carrying capacity of the
fields. For the hill men it is important to know the lambing
percentage, that is the number of lambs produced per 100 ewes,
and also to have details of the numbers and prices of the lambs
sold.

More and more importance is being attached to this matter
of keeping business records on farms, so much so, in fact, that the
Government has given some financial encouragement to do so.
From these records the farmer can compare one year with
another, benefit from his mistakes, or correct things that may
have gone wrong in some particular enterprise on the farm.

Because of the impact of the climate and of the elevation of
some hill or upland farms this matter of coping with winter
problems has been getting more and more attention.

The housing of stock, and not just in the winter-time, has
become one of the most important problems and one to which
a vast amount of research and investigation has been applied.

Depending on the geographical situation, on the breed of stock or other factors, some of the bigger animals must spend varying parts of the winter inside, that is except for the hardy breeds of hill breeding stock which can stay out the year round. But the dairy herds and the intensive beef herds are housed for considerable periods.

The dairy herds require a great deal of attention in feeding and milking, which is done twice a day, and in the handling of the milk they produce. For many years the normal method of housing dairy cows was to keep them in cowsheds where each cow was tied up in its own stall, where they were fed, milked and cleaned. This involved a lot of labour, and as wages rose considerable research was done on how to cheapen the costs of milk production while maintaining a high rate of production. This has been achieved in several ways, and we can give some examples. An important element of food for dairy cows is the silage made from the summer grass. Carrying it to individual cows was a heavy and costly job. In some cases this cost has been greatly reduced by so arranging the silage pit in proximity to the cowshed that the cows have constant access to the silage and help themselves to as much as they want under a system of 'self-feed' silage.

Alongside this, many dairies now operate the yard and parlour system, which is also easy to understand. It simply means that instead of being housed in individual stalls the milk cows live in a huge covered yard, often open at one end, where they have shelter and a deep straw bed, and when milking-time comes they file into the milking-parlour. It is amazing how soon the cows become disciplined to this system. There is a variation of this which is half-way between the yard and the tied stall and it is called the cow cubicle. In this system the cows have their own cubicles in which they can lie down separately, but they do not need to be tied. It all helps to keep the cow happy and productive.

In addition to these labour-saving systems of feeding and housing there have been changes in the handling of the milk. On all modern dairy farms the system of hand-milking has given way to machine-milking, and while many farms still put their milk into large churns, more and more are turning to bulk handling of milk. Under this system the milk is piped direct from the milking-machine into a bulk tank from which a big tanker from the Milk Marketing Board collects it.

The keeping of large numbers of cows indoors brought other problems such as the disposal of the manure. The normal bedding is straw, but in some areas and in some seasons it is hard to come by and peat, sawdust, and wood shavings have been used, and these are especially easy to use in the cubicle system. Another method is to keep the cows on slats on which the cows can walk while the dung and urine drop into a gathering-area below. This manure is often turned into liquid manure and pumped onto the fields, or where the ground is too soft pumped into pits until the land is dry enough to take tractors.

As has been said, cows spend varying times in these yards or cubicles, depending on the system followed on the farm. Normally the cows spend the winter inside and go out in the spring to the grass on which they spend the summer. But some farms have adopted a 'zero-grazing' system, although it is not in general use. This is another self-explanatory term which means no grazing. Under it, all the grassland is used for the very intensive production of silage, which is fed to the stock inside, and they only get out for exercise.

It must not be assumed that all farmers are turning to these modern methods, for some believe it is important to give stock individual attention, because they also believe that this way they get the best production from the stock. On all farms where there are important livestock enterprises such as dairying or beef production this matter of stockmanship is looked on as one of the most important factors in the operation of producing milk or beef. Whatever system is used, it is emphasized over and over again that no system of itself is a substitute for good stockmanship and good herd management.

The main advantage of these modern techniques is that they permit one man to look after more cows. The best results are obtained where the most modern systems are allied to this quality of stockmanship for which Scottish herdsmen are renowned. They believe that the animals are individuals and when treated as such give the best results. This matter of the management of different farms under different systems provides just one of the hundreds of examples which show farming to be very much an individual business. A whole section of the industry, such as dairying may follow any one of the different techniques available to it from the results of research and the investigation of new housing, management and recording systems, but each farmer must apply the knowledge and techniques available to his herd and his farm. There can be no hard and fast rule as to what will be right in any given set of circumstances. In order to achieve the best results part of one system will often be adapted to integrate with a slightly different method. So much will depend on the farmer's individual preference and on such things as the conditions of climate, soil, labour supply, and state of the farm buildings with which he has to cope. Distance from a suitable market can also exert a great influence on trends which develop from time to time and create a change in the farming pattern.

In Orkney, for example, there was a vastly inflated wartime population of Service personnel and the island farmers turned to milk production in a big way in order to meet the consequent demand which had suddenly arisen. But when these thousands of sailors, soldiers, and airmen suddenly departed at the end of the war this new market equally as suddenly disappeared. The island farmers who had geared themselves to milk production could not overnight turn to some other system and, as a result, a considerable line in Orkney cheese was developed, and this is now in great demand as a quality product.

There is one product in which Scotland has a really famous name—Scotch beef. The label 'Prime Scotch' is an accolade in the world's biggest market for fresh meat, the great Smithfield Market in London, and this accolade brings first-quality Scotch beef a premium or just that extra price over other types of beef.

The best Scotch beef is produced from the main beef breeds, with which we shall deal in some detail later—and by traditional individual methods in which, again, stockmanship is one of the most important factors. By road and rail great quantities of Scotch beef go daily to Smithfield Market.

But we cannot produce enough beef by what may be called the traditional methods to meet the great demand for beef from the great cities of the south, so farmers have been turning not only to more intensive methods of beef production but to methods which do not employ the traditional breeds and crosses of cattle used for the production of 'Prime Scotch'.

One approach to this problem of increasing our beef supplies has been to produce more beef from our dairy herds. In the traditional dairy herd it was the accepted practice for a farmer to rear all the heifer calves born on the farm. Such a heifer, as a young cow is called, would 'come into profit' by starting to produce milk when her first calf was born. At this time some of these heifers would be brought into the herd to replace older cows, whilst those which were not required for this herd replacement would be sold.

Dairy animals, however, are not always suitable for fattening into beef, so that when a farmer decides to produce beef from his dairy herd he uses a bull of a beef breed on some of the cows. The cross-bred calves thus produced make good beef animals and about three-quarters of the animals now being reared for beef come from the dairy herd.

In dairy herds where this policy has been adopted, sufficient of the best cows are still mated to dairy bulls to ensure an adequate number of heifers for eventual herd replacement.

Another way of combining milk and beef production is to make more use of what are called dual-purpose breeds, which, as their name implies, are breeds which give a lot of milk, but which also have a big beef potential. In such herds all the heifer calves will develop into satisfactory milking cows and all the bull calves will be suitable for beef. Of this type of cattle the British Friesian breed now predominates.

All the individual animals of any one breed, however, are not exactly alike. Within breeds there are different strains and in the Friesian there are many strains of good dual-purpose stock, giving plenty of milk while producing calves which can be fattened for beef. The unwanted calves of a Friesian herd need not be slaughtered at birth, but can be kept on as beef animals.

There is a straight economic advantage in getting a dairy

calf for beef production, whether it be a cross or a Friesian—
and some Friesian strains are also crossed with beef bulls by
the way—for this way the cost of the calf is cheaper. Under the
traditional method of producing beef from a beef herd, the
breeding cows produce only beef calves, so the cost of keeping
and feeding the mother must be reckoned in the cost of the calf.
But with the dairy cross or dual-purpose calf a large part of the
'overhead' cost of producing the calf is borne by the income
from the milk which the mother produces.

This business of producing these calves is now an important
industry within an industry, as it were, and there are special
organizations set up by farming co-operatives or auction marts
to provide 'calf banks' to ensure a steady supply of calves for
fattening for beef.

Two developments in modern farming have made it possible
to exploit this type of production by providing the right sort of
calf for the purpose required. One has been the use of artificial
insemination, a technique which has enabled farmers to use the
best bulls which they could not have afforded to buy themselves.
It has also enabled them to select a dairy bull for use on those
cows from which they want to breed herd replacements and a
beef bull for the remainder without the expense of either buying
or keeping a bull on the farm.

The other big development is 'barley beef', which, like so
many of the terms we have used, is self-explanatory, for it simply
means the production of beef by intensive feeding of barley.

The feeding of cereals to stock is not new, but it is fair to say
that what we know as the barley-beef system was developed in
Scotland at the Rowett Research Institute at Aberdeen by a
team headed by Dr T. R. Preston. The idea in itself was simple.
Barley was a relatively cheap cereal, produced in large quantities in Scotland, so why not use it to produce beef by feeding it
to cattle housed intensively and fattened from birth. This last
was important, as it cuts out the 'store' period in beef-cattle
production. This store period was that part of an animal's life
where it was fed enough to maintain itself until it was sold for
proper fattening procedure on a lowland fattening farm.

Barley beef aimed to produce beef stock in large numbers at

rather younger ages and from types of stock which might not otherwise have been considered for beef production. This was much easier said than done, for when animals are kept together in large numbers inside in relatively crowded conditions the risk of disease increases dramatically, and packing their stomachs with one main ingredient, in this case barley, could lead to disastrous problems caused by digestive disorders. So considerable research and trials work were undertaken on what other elements might be fed along with the barley, and in what condition the barley should be when fed.

In time the worst snags were overcome and the term 'barley beef' came into the British farming language. It is not claimed that barley-beef has all the flavour of the traditional prime Scotch, but it does produce a tender type of meat of attractive colour and reasonable quality relatively cheaply.

Perhaps the chief attribute of barley beef is the fact that, by intensification of production, the farmer can put the finished product on to the market at a lower price, which is always a factor to be considered by the consumer, and the considerable market which exists for it speaks for itself.

While the dairy and many of the beef herds are in their winter quarters the hill farmers producing hill cattle or sheep will be thinking of the spring and the arrival of the calves and the lambs, so we shall now have a look at the hill farms and the preparations for spring.

CHAPTER 7

PREPARATIONS FOR SPRING

IT has already been shown that a very large proportion of the land of Scotland—about two-thirds, in fact—is described as uplands or rough grazings, and while the output of these areas is not, in terms of yields of crops or livestock products per acre, anything like that of the Lowland and more intensive farms, they form a very important element in Scottish farming, for, as we have seen, the hills are 'the reservoir' for the large quantities of lambs and calves which form the raw material for the production of beef and lamb and mutton fattened on the richer lands.

Because of the conditions of climate and elevation it has been said that the Scottish hill-sheep industry is the most 'tradition-bound' sector of Scottish farming, the inference being that the physical conditions made it difficult for the hill-sheep farmer to change his methods. But even here we shall show that changes have, in fact, taken place and that more are in the air.

Here it is necessary to mention a chapter of Scottish history before we can understand the spread and size of the great hill-sheep industry of the country. Until the end of the Jacobite Rising on the field of Culloden, near Inverness, vast areas of the Highlands were controlled by the clans and their chiefs. It was the power of these chiefs, many of whom played a part in the rising, that the Government set out to break, so the hereditary judicial rights of the chiefs were abolished in 1747, and this made the importance of the chiefs dependent on their wealth and not on the numbers of men they could marshal.

This led to a scramble to increase the value of the estates, and in many cases, as Dr Johnson put it after his tour in the Highlands, this led to the 'degeneration of the chiefs from patriarchial rulers to rapacious landlords'.

It was found that the quickest and cheapest way to do this

was to turn the hills over to sheep, and this led to 'The Clearances', when literally thousands of the small farmer or crofter families who populated the glens and straths were forcibly cleared from the land which had been their homes for generations. This tragic chapter in Scottish history had two by-products—it created the vast hill-sheep industry and it resulted in extensive colonization by Scots in many Commonwealth countries, particularly Canada.

So the Blackface and Cheviot sheep multiplied and spread over the hills to such an extent that in some areas the value of the grazings fell until another source of income was found by letting the deer forests for stalking. But the sheep maintained their hold over several million acres of uplands and today still produce huge numbers of lambs for fattening on the low ground. These breeds became the hardy acclimatized inhabitants of the hills and moors from the green upland of the Borders to the flat heaths of Caithness.

Over the years a system of hill-sheep husbandry developed and while the big times for the flockmasters and their shepherds were at the lambings in the spring and the clippings later in the summer, the hill-sheep year really began in or around November. Depending on the area, it is at about this time that the rams are put out on the hill to mate with the ewes for the production of the lambs in the spring. And as the winter approached the very young ewes, the ewe hoggs, were taken off the higher hills to spend their first winter in kindlier conditions on low-ground farms. They went on to their native hills in the spring and stayed there until their productive career as hill mothers was ended.

This system of giving the young females a chance by letting them have their first winter on lower ground is known as 'wintering' the hoggs away. In this and in other aspects of hill-sheep farming the changes are coming. Perhaps the first big change came with the idea that the hill ewe, living a hard life on the high cold hills, often having to get down through the snow for the sparse vegetation, might benefit from a little concentrated feed, apart from the little hay which was sometimes given in the worst winters. The 'dyed-in-the-wool' farmers held up their hands in horror at the idea of giving hill sheep any special feed, as they held it would reduce their hardiness and stop them from foraging for their own food. But some pioneers tried it and, especially before lambing, the little concentrates fed did result in more and better lambs and fewer half-starved ewes unable to feed their lambs in the period between their arrival and the time the grass and other forage began to grow on the hills. That was one change.

Another now being tried more extensively is the wintering of the ewe hoggs at home by giving them some kind of shelter. The idea behind this was to reduce the cost of away wintering, which with rising transport costs and dearer grazing charges on the low ground was beginning to eat away much of any little profit the hill-sheep men could glean from their flocks. These wintering houses must be simple and cheap, for if they cost too much it would be just as dear to winter the hoggs at home as away on a lowland farm.

Other ways of improving the output of the hill flocks is in improving the ground on which they feed and by so controlling the grazing on the hills that one part of a hill is kept free of sheep, so that when the grass does come it comes away fast and is not kept down by being grazed before it has got a proper start.

The idea of keeping sheep indoors has led to the idea that they may not only be wintered but that some of the lambs could be fattened on an indoor system.

Lambing is naturally a busy time for the shepherds, starting earlier on the low-ground flocks, where the grass comes earlier and allows the ewes the feed to provide the milk for their lambs. In its demand for labour, however, one of the biggest events on a hill-sheep farm is the clipping, when the fleeces are sheared off the sheep to be sold for the making of tweeds or the provision of carpet or mattress wool. The wool of the Scottish Blackface is in great demand, for instance, in Italy for the packing of mattresses.

The traditional method of meeting this demand for many hands at shearing-time in the Highlands was by the system known as 'neighbouring', where the neighbouring staffs combined on the different farms and each got on with the job of

Plate 9 *Two combine harvesters at work in Perthshire.* (*Photo Cowper, Perth.*)

Plate 10 *Spraying from a helicopter in Perthshire.* (*Photo Cowper, Perth.*)

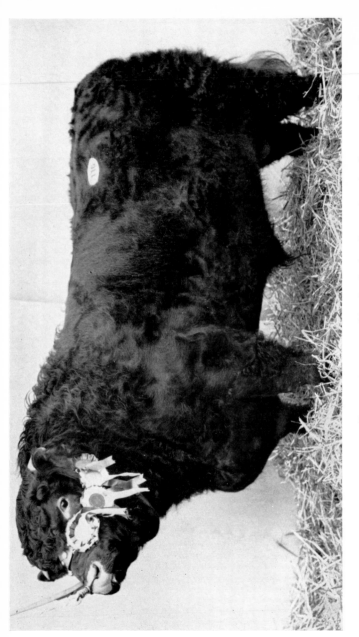

Plate 11 *A Beef Shorthorn Bull, Denend Ragusa, sold at Perth where it was champion for 10,000 guineas.*

Plate 12 *A Highland Bull, Gille Coir 2nd of Scone Palace. (Photo Cowper, Perth.)*

Plate 13 *Black Beckett of Barnoldby, Supreme and Senior Champion, bred by Messrs. Osmond & Sons Ltd., Barnoldby-le-Beck, Waltham, Nr. Grimsby, Lincs., and sold to L. L. O'Bryan, Lakewood Farms, Mukwonago, Wisconsin, U.S.A., for 10,000 guineas. (Photo Aberdeen-Angus Cattle Society.)*

removing the wool from flocks which may muster several thousand sheep. But here again things are changing with the arrival of the electric shears and easier transport facilities. Many hill-sheep farmers have their clipping done by teams provided by contractors. Many hill farmers and especially their wives, prefer this system, for the contractors come on the farm with their own feeding arrangements, thus saving the farmers' wives the problem of feeding hungry men. It was also possible that some of the neighbourings turned into somewhat rumbustious social events where on occasion things got a little out of control!

Long before the lambing and the clipping the work of preparation for the spring starts, in many cases away back in the winter, which is usually the time for catching up on many tasks for which there is no time in spring.

When the weather allows the ploughing will go on, starting, in many cases, as soon as the grain crops are off the ground, and it will go on until the fields are ready for the winter wheat, which is sown so that the seed lies in the ground during the winter, or for the spring sowings. Before the sowings the farmyard manure will have been driven out for the root crops or the fertilizers applied on the other land. Nowadays, when the cereal seeds are sown the fertilizer goes down into the drill along with the seed, combining two operations in one.

Also during the winter, when there may not be much other work for the farm staffs, the opportunity will be taken to see to the fences, to carry out some draining and do some ditching, to clean out the grain stores and driers thoroughly or check all the machinery, so that when the spring work arrives the farm and the staff and the machinery are on the top line ready for the busy times.

Fields may be surrounded by fences or hedges, or in some areas stone dikes. Some of the dikes may be ordinary stone and cement, but in many areas farm workers became specialists in 'dry-stone diking', which as its name implies means the making of dikes or walls using stones only. Many of these dikes were made from stones or rocks cleared from the fields. In recent years there has been a revival of interest in this old craft of dry-stone diking in Scotland. Some areas have their special problems when it comes to fencing. In the north, in Caithness, for instance, there is not a great deal of woodland and on many farms there the fields are surrounded by 'fences' of large flat stone slabs which are found locally in abundance.

The chemical fertilizers which the farmer puts on his ground are the product of a highly scientific industry where years of research have been devoted to producing fertilizers which will increase the productivity of the soil. The most modern fertilizers are called compound fertilizers, because they may have three different elements in varying forms. One compound may be high in nitrogen, another high in potash—which encourages the white clover in the grassland—and the clover in turn is useful for drawing nitrogen into the soil from the atmosphere and so provides the farmer with a cheap source of the nitrogen his grassland requires.

In some parts of Scotland spring comes very early, and there are some pockets of land in the south-west where the soil and the lack of frost make it possible to plant early potatoes long before other areas.

It will be seen from this that a great many farm activities overlap each other. The early-potato planting may be finished before many other crops are sown at all and, in turn, these potatoes will be ready early in the summer to catch a valuable market.

All sectors of farming life have seen dramatic changes in techniques and in methods of operation and this applies equally to the farmhouse. There was a time when the farmer's wife was as busy preserving foodstuffs for the family as her husband was in storing food for his stock, but while many wives still do a lot of preserving in jam and in other ways such as salting bacon or pork, it is more than likely that the storage will be done in a deep freeze. In some parts of the country there is real need for having ample food reserves. Even areas far from shopping centres are served by travelling shops, but there are some areas where heavy snow may cut them off for long periods, and in times of extreme difficulty helicopters have been used to bring food for the people and hay for the stock.

Long ago the traditional food stored used to be a chest of oatmeal and a barrel of salt herring, all of which meant work for the housewife. Today, however, there is a wide choice of preserved and tinned foods as well as those which can be kept in the refrigerator. As a result, the rural housewife now has more time on her hands and is often pleased to earn a little extra money for her family by helping with the potato-planting or the harvesting of the crop or by working part time at one of the intensive poultry units or by doing seasonal work at a milk creamery.

We have mentioned early potatoes in this chapter and for those special areas where they are grown they are a very important crop. But the maincrop potatoes are an important crop over very large areas of Scotland and for a very special reason. Because of its latitude, potato growers in Scotland are less troubled with aphids, the little insects which live on potato leaves and which can carry many potato diseases with them. As Scotland is relatively free of such problems, Scotch seed potatoes are in great demand in England. This is, in fact, quite a valuable 'export' trade and it is worth about £6,000,000 a year in sales to England.

In other words the Scottish potato-growers provide the large-scale potato-growers of the English Fenlands and other areas with their stock seed—their raw material for food production—rather like the hill farmers who provide the low-ground men with their calves and lambs for fattening.

CHAPTER 8

SPRING AT LAST

DIFFERENT people have their favourite seasons. With some it may be summer, others autumn, and there are others who like the winter for its contrast between a cosy fire and the hard weather outside. But on the farm spring is the exciting season, the season of promise, of awakening activity on all farming fronts.

Spring comes in the sunny hedgerows, with the lambs, with the last of the sowing and planting, when the snowdrops give way to primroses and other flowers, when the fields are alive with activity and the first flush of fresh green begins to shine in the pastures when the winter-sown wheat is beginning to stand up—all adding up to the truth that in the spring the countryside is a wonderful place to be in.

As with everything else, spring today contrasts with the springs of former years. Some may contrast the feverish activity of today with the more leisurely pace of former years, but the point to be borne in mind about modern farming is that it has vastly increased its productivity in all ways. There is today much more output per man and much more output per acre, there is more milk per cow, more hundredweights of grain from each acre, more stock carried per acre. To put it another way, we are farming more intensively. If we did not farm in this intensive way, we would produce much less food from our own fields, so that we would have to buy more from abroad, and as a nation we cannot afford this drain of cash from the country.

In a former chapter we made it clear that the timing of the various 'harvests' was necessary to maintain our supplies of milk all the year round and of our bacon, eggs, and beef and mutton, and so on.

While this cycle of production is necessary to maintain the flow of food, it is nevertheless a fact that spring is the main time for many of the farm stock to produce their young, and so we have the lambs and spring calves. As we have mentioned, there are moves afoot to fatten sheep inside and to 'stagger' the lambing so that out-of-season lamb production might catch a better market, but in general most of the lambs do not arrive until there is sufficient grass for their mothers to eat and so be able to produce the milk to maintain healthy lambs. Any other system of lamb production demands special housing and the feeding of expensive concentrates, as well as very special breeding techniques.

Spring can often be a worrying time for the farmer. Sometimes, just when it looks as if the grass is about to start growing, the wind will blow from the east for days, and sometimes weeks, at a time. Unlike the south-west wind, which comes in over the Atlantic, bringing warmth and moisture, the east wind blows from across the north European plain, that flat land which is so cold in winter or in late spring that it reminds farmers on the east coast that there is nothing between them and the Ural Mountains.

It will help if the hedges are well kept to provide shelter, or some farmers may have gone even further and planted shelter belts of woodland to protect the stock in the fields from any bad prevailing wind. In fact, many Scottish farmers are showing great interest in this type of forestry, which provides a 'crop' which adds to the value of the farm and also brings this valuable advantage of shelter for the stock.

It is obvious that the 3,000,000 lambs born in Scotland every year do not all arrive at the same time. In the 'in-by' land of the sheltered Border valleys, lambing will have started before the snow is off the lower hills and the later lambing time creeps northward so that the lambs may be arriving on the high hills of Sutherland when the Border lambs are well-grown and strong.

If the winter has been mild and the spring early and fine, there should be little to worry the sheep farmer, but the winter may have been a severe one and the spring late and cold. This could mean that the ewes are not at full strength for the arrival of their lambs and are not completely fitted or the task of feeding them, because their milk is poor and there is little of it.

The lamb itself may be weak and may need feeding from a bottle to help to give it a start in life. The death of a lamb means the loss for a whole year of the income from the ewe, for when the store sale time comes that lamb would be worth £5 or £6 and the loss of a number of lambs in a bad year would eat heavily into the farmer's financial resources. In one recent very bad year lamb losses on some hill farms were running at an average of about 20 per cent, with, in some bad cases, farmers losing half their lamb crop, and lambs are a 'crop' just as any other farm product is.

So every effort is made by the flockmasters and their shepherds to produce healthy lambs, by providing adequate shelter, also by giving the ewes a little extra feed just before lambing and also by inoculations. The veterinary scientists have been a great help to the sheep farmers in this way and lambs may be given what is called a 'seven-shot' inoculation, which means that in the one administration the lamb is protected against seven different diseases or troubles, such as lamb dysentery, pulpy kidney, braxy, and so on.

Different breeds of sheep vary in their production of lambs, some having sets of twins time after time and others, especially hill sheep, having one lamb only. The production of lambs from a flock is expressed in the percentage of lambs per 100 ewes. A Lowland flock with many twins or even a few triplets could have a lambing percentage of 150, and that is 150 lambs per 100 ewes, while a hill flock where a few lambs may die in difficult conditions may have 80 per cent, or even 60 per cent.

The more intensive the production the more is it necessary for a high standard of management or stockmanship. Sometimes when a lamb dies the shepherd will take away one of the twins from a ewe that has had two lambs and persuade the mother of the dead lamb to rear the other one. This is not easy to do and shepherds try many ruses to achieve this. One is to skin the dead lamb and tie its skin on the spare lamb, so that the mother is deceived by smell into thinking that this is her original lamb.

Some days after they are born the ram lambs are castrated if they are to be sold for fattening. It is about this time that the lambs and ewes get these injections we have already mentioned.

This does not end the steps which farmers in some areas must take to ensure healthy flocks. Some pastures suffer from 'mineral deficiency', in other words a shortage of certain mineral elements which are necessary to keep sheep healthy. Some of these elements are no more than trace elements in the soil, but if they are not there and, in turn, do not get into the feed, the sheep will pine or die.

For instance, considerable areas of the north of Scotland where thousands of sheep are bred, are deficient in cobalt. This also applies to some of the hill grazings from Bodmin Moor in Cornwall to these areas where sheep are bred in the north of Scotland. This deficiency leads to sheep pining, to poor and dying lambs. It is remedied by applying small quantities of the element per acre or giving the mineral to the ewes and lambs.

The lowland flocks lamb in specially built shelters, sometimes of straw bales or thatched hurdles with a hut nearby for the shepherd or 'the lambing man', who may be specially employed at this season. Some farmers prefer these temporary erections to permanent lambing sheds, because of the disease risk in using a permanent structure every year—but provided these structures are throughly disinfected there is no risk.

A problem of lamb production is the arrival of so many lambs at the same time, so that when the time comes to sell them there could be a glut on the market. A way to overcome this is to have some feed stored or some extra pasture to hold the lambs off the market until the prices improve. The Lowland lambs are usually heavier than the hill lambs, but here is a great demand for the small, attractive hill lambs as they do produce really tasty flesh.

Some mention has been made of efforts to increase or intensify sheep production by fattening sheep or lambs inside buildings. Another way is to intensify the grazing, by keeping more ewes and lambs per acre. This has been achieved by a new idea in sheep management called forward-creep grazing. A field is divided into a number of paddocks by means of sheep netting with a gate leading from each paddock into the next. Each gate has a spar at the bottom which can be moved up or down. By this means the farmer can leave enough space for the lambs to creep through to the next paddock. This space, however, is too small for the ewes to get through.

All the ewes and lambs are put together into one of the paddocks, which enables the lambs either to stay with their mothers to have milk or to creep through into the next paddock to have first bite at the grass before the ewes can get it. After about four days the paddock where the ewes are grazing is bare and they are then moved into the next paddock. At the same time the spar is raised in the next gate so that the lambs can still be 'creeping' ahead to have first bite at the next lot of grass whilst the ewes are clearing up what the lambs have left uneaten. The ewes and lambs are moved round the six paddocks every four days in this way so that by the time they get back to the first paddock the grass has had twenty days rest and has come away again. One advantage of this movement of the stock and resting of the pasture is that any worms left on the grass from the lambs' stomachs will have been dead by the time the sheep come back on to it. There will therefore be no danger of reinfestation through the lambs picking up the larvae of worms again when they are grazing.

The sheep like being moved on to fresh grass frequently. One old country saying is that the sheep should not hear the church bells twice from the same field. In other words if the sheep are in one field on a Sunday when the bells are rung they should be in another field by the time Sunday and the ringing of the bells comes round again.

This intensive grazing system using paddocks needs a lush supply of grass, so this makes it necessary for the lambing to be timed so that it is late enough to coincide with the growth of the grass.

The lambs will be sold for the butcher as soon as they are ready and a fresh set or sets of lambs will go on to the grass. This intensive method of production means that lambs will not be at full weight when they are sold, but more of them will be sold, so that even if they do not make the top price the turnover in numbers, and therefore of income, will be bigger. Once again it means a greater output per acre or a bigger contribution of food from the same acreage of land. This method of intensive grazing also means that the other pastures can be used for maximum output of silage for storing for winter feed.

On the hill farms the spring will see the hill cows calving and here the farmer will like to see the calves come as early as grazing and other conditions will allow, so that they will be big and strong when they come to be sold at the autumn sales. Late calves would be that much smaller and make smaller prices.

If they come late and are small, the farmer may have to keep them over the winter, which not only means extra expense in feeding but it means they will take up housing space where the in-calf cows will be wintering. On many farms the cows stay out all the winter, but on others the farmers have built open shelters, large houses open at the end away from the prevailing wind in which the stock can shelter during the worst storms.

Those farmers who have enough low ground to produce winter feed in the form of silage or hay, will, as a matter of policy, keep all their calves through the winter, which brings two advantages. First the calves are much bigger through being a full year old in the following spring, and secondly, they will be going on to the market when the grass is coming away and their buyers have grazings waiting for them.

Here again it will be seen that conditions dictate the farming policy to be followed. The hill farmer with insufficient food for both cows and calves will have to sell his calves in the autumn, but the farmer who can winter both cows and calves will do so. Other deciding factors are buildings, labour supply, and so on, but these are just a few of the factors the farmer takes into consideration when making his decisions.

The beef herds in the Lowlands are managed much in the same way, except that some of them calve in the autumn, which means the weaned calves are bigger when sold the following autumn and make more money than the spring-born calves sold at the same time.

The calves from the Highlands come to the southern markets for sale to the feeders in trainloads or in huge road trucks—changed days indeed from the times when they were driven on foot all the way. Until the coming of the railways, cattle droving was one of the most important farming activities in Scotland, and these cattle covered vast distances. Those from the islands would be taken across in boats or made to swim across the narrower stretches of water between the islands and the mainland. Some of these narrow pieces of water are called kyles and even today those attractive shaggy Highland cattle are affectionately known as 'kyloes' because of the memories of the days when they swam the kyles.

So huge herds would be driven slowly over the Grampians or down through the western passes to the great fairs or cattle trysts as they were called.

The droves of cattle were in charge of a special race of men called drovers and very often they would stay with the cattle after they were bought and drive them down to the destinations in England, say in the Fens for fattening. The drover's year could start with taking a large number of cattle from the Highlands to the Lowlands, continuing with them to the South of England, where they were fattened for sale at Smithfield market, and as the drover arrived about harvest he would hire himself for that harvest and then set off, on foot, usually on the long haul north.

CHAPTER 9

ON THE LAND IN SPRING

W E have shown that modern farming is an intensive, science-based industry in which the activity reaches its crescendo in the spring, when conditions are right for all the things that must be done. And conditions *must* be right. Ploughing cannot start until the ground is dry enough and when it has been ploughed it is left until completely dry and cultivated by dragging harrows over it, breaking the soil down to what the farmer calls a good 'tilth', which means the soil is in good condition to take the seed. For this job a good drying wind is welcome, but not too much of it, for it could cause the grassland to check its growth and a really strong drying wind could blow the surface soil away on light soils, and here we have one of the many examples of how there is a conflict between the conditions the farmer wants.

Moist weather would be good for the young grass, but not so good for the preparation of the seed-bed for the grain, so when conditions permit the farmer gets on with the job as fast as possible.

What the farmer sows and plants will be decided by the land and the average weather conditions, and we have shown that the south-west is a dairying area because the conditions are good for grass while on the rich soils of the eastern seaboard there are the crops of cereals, potatoes, sugar-beet, and so on.

The main cereal crop in Scotland is barley, which accounts for about 45 per cent of the total crop of cereals—wheat, barley, and oats. The acreage of barley has been rising in recent years to meet the demand for the production of barley-beef cattle. The acreage of wheat is relatively small in Scotland and while the acreage of oats is still large it is much smaller than it used to be. But there is a chance that oats could come back into favour for two reasons. One is that those farmers who grow barley continuously run the risk of getting disease in the crop, whereas by putting oats into the system they can provide a break crop and still produce a cash crop of grain. The second reason is that some new varieties of oats bred in Scandinavia can give much higher yields and as some Scottish soils are good for oat-growing the view is that the steady decline in the oat acreage may be halted. Changing food habits among the people was also a reason for the decline in oat-growing. Porridge is still a favourite food for many Scots, but not to the extent it was. One reason is that the modern housewife prefers the ready-made packeted cereals to the oats which require time and care in cooking.

It may surprise many people that so many of these new varieties of cereals—even oats—are bred on the Continent and not here. The reason for this is that for many years a breeder who produced a new variety of plant on the Continent could 'register' it and he obtained royalties from the people who bought it for further propagation, just like an inventor who patents a machine. Until very recently there were no 'plant breeders' rights' in Britain, so there was not much financial incentive for anyone, whether an individual or a research station, to produce a new variety, for once the first lot was bought the buyer could go on reproducing it himself. But we have plant breeders' rights here now and we should see more effort directed at producing new varieties in this country.

The main use to which barley is put in Scotland is the feeding of stock, but the better-quality types are used in brewing and distilling, two very big industries in Scotland and very big users of Scottish-produced grain.

There is a saying that the best distilling barley should be grown within sight of the sea, but wherever it is grown it is transported to the famous distilling areas such as Speyside and its tributary valleys of Glenlivet, Glenfiddich, and so on, which have world-famous names for the production of whisky.

The whisky made in these northern glens is malt, that is it is produced from malt made from barley and from a distilling process. Alcohol can also be made from other grains, such as maize, by an industrial process which also produces whisky. While connoisseurs prefer these Highland malt whiskies, they are not to everyone's taste, so the malt whisky is blended with the grain whisky to produce a huge variety of blends. This blending process, apart from helping to meet the tastes of those who do not like malt whiskies, has another purpose—it brings up the total quantity of whisky. There would not be enough malt whisky to supply the total demand, but when it is blended with the larger quantities of grain whisky the malt helps to maintain quality and taste while increasing the quantity.

We have already seen how there are conflicts within farming and the production of cereals provides another. Naturally the farmer who grows feeding barley wants as high a price for it as possible, but it is estimated that for every barley-grower who wants as high a price as possible for his barley there are four cattlemen who want their stockfeed as cheap as possible and barley and oats are important elements in these feeds. For it must be remembered that about 80 per cent of all Scottish farm produce—worth about £200,000,000, remember—is in the form of livestock or livestock products.

Most of the cereal crop is now harvested by means of the combine-harvester, popularly referred to as the 'Combine' because it combines the two operations of cutting the corn and threshing the grain. The combine works at such a speed that the market cannot possibly absorb all the corn at once, and indeed it is not desirable to flood the market, for a glut will only cause the inevitable drop in price.

So the use of a combine, itself expensive, calls for special facilities for drying and storing the grain. It also calls for different types of cereal, with strong straw to stand up for a long time without going down. The combine cuts the corn, pushes out the straw behind it, and delivers the grain into sacks which are left in the field to be picked up by a following tractor, or it delivers the grain in bulk into a tank or a trailer by which it is conveyed to the store on the farm. The store is important, as it allows a more even flow of grain on to the market and, in fact, there is official encouragement for farmers by way of a bonus for selling their grain under a forward contract, under which the buyer knows it is there and that he can collect it at a future date when he wants it.

Some farmers still use the older reaper-and-binder for harvesting, a machine which cuts the corn and binds it into sheaves. These are stooked in the field until dry enough to be carted to the cornyard, where they are built into stacks which remain until wanted, when they are threshed on the spot.

It is still possible to see on many farms these orderly rows of stacks or ricks, and some farmers take great pride in the line and appearance of these ricks.

One practice connected with the sowing of the cereal crops is the sowing of grass and clover seeds so that when the cereals are harvested the sward is getting a good start. The grass seeds are sown shortly after the cereal has been sown or even after it is up through the ground and firmly rooted enough for harrowing. The creation of grass pastures after cereal-growing gives the land a rest and when stock graze on the grass it helps to raise the fertility. In due course the grass would be ploughed up again and in this way the farmer turns the fertility into cash.

The idea of undersowing cereals with grass is that the cereals will protect the young grass and when the time to harvest the cereals comes the cutting knife travels above the height of the young grass and this is why some fields are green very quickly after harvest-time.

In a wet season there is a risk of the grass shooting up through the corn, so that at harvest-time a lot of young green grass is mixed with the corn, which will require a considerable amount of drying.

Also in very wet seasons the undersown pasture could be damaged by the wheels of the combine, which is a heavy machine, so this practice of undersowing cannot be carried out in certain districts. In these conditions farmers prefer to cut the harvest as quickly as possible, plough the stubble, and sow the grass seed, which means there would be no autumn grazing from such fields, as with those which had been undersown, but there should be a well-established pasture by the following spring.

There are several other crops which are sown in the spring and they come under the general term of root or green crops, which are very useful for feeding livestock in the winter. These crops will include kale and rape and turnips and swedes and mangolds, but mangolds are not grown very extensively in Scotland. The acreage of turnips has also been decreasing because of the problems of handling these root crops, which demand hard work at hoeing and are not very easy to harvest. But here, too, science and engineering have come to the rescue and could mean that turnips, which are excellent stockfeed, could regain some popularity.

By sowing the seed properly spaced, hoeing is made much easier, or mechanized, or it may even be made unnecessary, and mechanical harvesters are available for handling turnips. Lifting by hand and topping and tailing them with a knife and throwing them into a cart on a bitterly cold winter day was not a popular job with workers who earlier in the season may have been standing in long rows, hoeing the same turnips under a boiling sun.

The kale or rape seed is broadcast on the ground and harrowed in and grazed off in the winter. The tall green kale is easily distinguished and it is very popular with the stock. Often the kale is fed to dairy cattle and the rape used for fattening lambs.

The growing of the turnips and swedes involves considerable work in preparation and drilling of the ground, and the hoeing or singling, as it is called, the idea being to remove unwanted plants and leave single plants standing at set distances apart, so that when they fill out they will have plenty of room in the drill. Turnips may be eaten off on the ground or carted to clamps or other storage sites. It is true they are still a difficult crop to cultivate, manage and harvest, but, with so much cultivation, drilling, hoeing, and lifting they are also a good 'cleaning' crop for the ground. Where they are eaten off they are also an aid to fertility.

Apart from the problems of dealing with turnips, they have been decreasing in acreage for another reason—silage, which is also an excellent winter-feed standby and, moreover, is a crop which can be mechanized from beginning to end.

Apart from this competition from silage as an alternative feed and the problems of management of the crop, farmers shy off turnips for yet another reason. They can be attacked by insects and the plants destroyed, which could mean that a crop may have to be sown a second time. To prevent this insect attack it is possible to treat the seed with chemicals before sowing, so that the plants will not be attacked as they come through the ground.

In short, turnips are not only a crop which presents problems of management and handling, they are also expensive in labour, and finance is a subject to which farmers have been forced to pay increasing attention.

But in spite of all this there are still many farmers who have a firm belief in the value of turnips as stockfeed, and they are the ones who are persisting with them, using all the aids which modern science and engineering provide, to make the job of producing turnips much easier than it was a few decades ago.

There seems little doubt that as these new ideas in dealing with the turnip crop bring a reduction in the trouble and cost of its production this crop could stage a strong comeback among arable farmers who have large livestock enterprises on their farms.

Plate 14 *Ayrshire Heifers at BOCM South Cathkin Farm taking part in milking trials run in conjunction with the Scottish Milk Marketing Board. (Photo BOCM.)*

Plate 15 *A Belted Galloway cow and her calf going up for sale on an East Lothian farm.*

Plate 16 *Dairy cattle helping themselves at the face of a self-feeding silage pit. Note how space is saved by straw bales being stacked above the silage. (Photo S.A.I. Ltd.)*

Plate 17 *A group of cows of the new Luing Breed on their native island in the Western Isles. (Photo Cowper, Perth.)*

Plate 18 *Ayrshire cows on a rich clover pasture in Midlothian.* (*Photo S.A.I. Ltd.*)

CHAPTER 10

SUMMER AND GRASS

IN some of the very favoured parts of the south-west the early potatoes will have been planted even before spring proper has arrived and one of the signs that spring is passing into summer is the enrichment of the foliage of these early potatoes, or 'new' potatoes as they are called to differentiate them from the main crops, which, stored in clamps or in buildings, have sustained the market for this important food all through the winter.

About the middle of May the farmers in the favoured areas of Wales will be hoping to lift their crops of earlies and, a little later, the Scottish production will be coming off the fields, lifted usually by organized companies of workers who may be the womenfolk from neighbouring farms or perhaps Irish workers who come over for this task.

The timing of the lifting of the early potato crop is vitally important from the financial point of view for the farmer. Housewives are prepared to pay a good deal more for the first of the new potatoes, but if the home crop does not arrive on time it could find itself in competition with imported early potatoes from Mediterranean countries, and from the Channel Islands. This market is very sensitive to supply and demand, so that it is possible to see potatoes selling at £30, or much more, a ton in the first week or two, but dropping to about half that or even much less in a very short time as the flow of supplies on to the market increases. Our own farmers can be very annoyed if they find the profitability of their early-potato crop diminished by this overseas competition.

The lifting of the early potatoes is one of the many country-side jobs which provide extra income for farming families or townspeople who live near the farms, and this is even more the case when it comes to the harvesting of the main crop in the autumn.

But there is another avenue for extra revenue for country people which indicates the changing pattern of our lives, not only in the countryside, but in the towns and cities. As the national standard of living increases, people have not only more money to spend but more opportunities and encouragement to travel, and farmers' wives or farm workers' wives have set out to cater for this extra trade by providing accommodation. In the case of farms there is official publication of information about farm holidays and along many country roadsides, especially near the sea or the famous scenic areas like the Highlands, many country folk are catering for this tourist trade and many are the signs to be seen offering 'Bed and Breakfast'.

In fact, this tourist industry is officially encouraged among the smallest of Scotland's 'farmers', the crofters, of whom there are about 20,000 in what are called the seven crofting counties of the Highlands and islands. Tourism has become a recognized method of adding to the income of the crofters many of whose smallholdings do not provide enough income to maintain the family, or enough full-time work. With official encouragement crofters have either extended their houses to provide this extra accommodation or have built little chalets to house the passing tourists.

So the changing patterns of the fields mark the arrival of the summer—mainly a variation of greens as different plants begin to fill out in their foliage like the potatoes or the turnips or the grasses and the cereals.

The grass is coming away strongly on the lowland farms and as the hill pastures have become more productive the hoggs which have been wintered away will have gone back on to their native hills, while cattle which have been housed in the winter will have been turned out to the fields, making their management and feeding easier and simpler.

This flush of grass brings with it a flush of milk production and the collecting services will be busy—whether they are collecting in the churns which are set out at the roadsides or in the big bulk tankers under the system which cuts out the handling of these churns. This is a very busy time for the creameries which turn the surplus liquid milk into butter or cheese or milk powder. Unlike England and Wales, which are covered by one big Milk Marketing Board, Scotland has three milk marketing boards, one covering a large area of the country from Angus, Perth, and Argyll to the Borders, one for the north-east at Aberdeen, and one for the north at Inverness, and this one has a creamery in the Orkney Islands, already referred to.

These marketing boards regulate the marketing of milk where the main problem is dealing with the milk not needed for the liquid market—mainly milk for drinking or putting in tea or coffee, etc. This surplus goes for manufacture, as we have seen, into butter, cheese, or milk powder. This regulation of the liquid and manufacturing milk is difficult, as we get so much of our butter and cheese from overseas, so that there is a limit to the size of the market for these products. Milk going for manufacture makes a much smaller price than milk going to be bottled for the liquid market, so there is a system of limiting production by price—as decided at the Price Review discussed in Chapter 4.

What happens is that the Government officials and the farmers' leaders decide on a quantity which will be enough to supply the liquid market and this is called the standard quantity, which gets the full agreed price. Any surplus for manufacture gets a much smaller price and the average of these two prices is known as the pool price, which is the price actually paid to the farmer. So it will be seen that if far too much milk is produced and a high proportion of it goes for manufacture the pool price will be depressed and many farmers, the ones who are not the most efficient, will not think it worth while continuing in milk production, and the fact that they go out of production tends to reduce the supplies. This works up to a point where the departure of producers is often masked by the fact that those left in milk production are getting more efficient and they are getting more milk from the same number of cows. But it is a fact that when the milk price is kept low enough to reduce the profitability, production will drop, and there have been times when this drop has been serious enough to jeopardize the supply even of liquid milk.

These creameries where the butter and cheese are made are

huge, scrupulously clean plants handling thousands of gallons of milk a day. When the milk is made into butter it is first of all separated, the cream being made into butter, while the skim milk, left after the separation of the cream, makes good feeding for calves and pigs. Pigs do well on skim milk mixed with barley meal. Cheese is still made on several farms in the south-west of Scotland and one of the problems of cheese-making is disposal of another by-product, the whey, which contains about one-third of the net energy value of milk, and a gallon has about the same value as a pound of cereal meal. But it does not keep well and it has a high water content where it is produced in large quantities. It can be fed to pigs and calves, however, so that pig-keeping is a useful adjunct on a farm which makes cheese.

It will be obvious that with so much grass available summer is the time when milk is cheapest to produce. Milk is therefore paid for to the farmer on a seasonal scale which gives him a higher price in winter when the cost of producing milk is higher and lower in summer when the cost of production is cheaper. Later on we shall be referring to the setting up of the milk marketing boards, whose job it is to ensure as far as possible an adequate supply of milk to the housewife and also to ensure that while there are variations of price to the farmer through the different seasons there is little or no variation in the price to the consumer.

This brings us to another example where conditions will decide whether a farmer should concentrate his production in winter or summer. Where grass is very plentiful he might opt for summer production, but where he has to buy in a proportion of his feed he might concentrate on winter production.

An important factor in the use of grass for feeding to cattle, especially dairy cattle, is conservation, keeping, and storing it until it is wanted, for on most farms there would be too much grass for the cows to eat during the summer and if the farmer kept enough cows to eat all the summer grass he would have an even bigger problem in having to buy in a lot more—and more expensive—food for them in the winter. The main methods of grass conservation are hay and silage. Hay is very popular with the farmers and the cows, as it is easy to handle and when well made has a good feeding value, but with the average climate of Britain, where we might get rain at the wrong time, haymaking may be difficult. Even so making hay is one of the big tasks of high summer. After the new potatoes it is the next 'harvest', to be followed by the cereals and later by the main-crop potatoes and sugar-beet.

For the farmer who prefers hay to silage, the scientist and the engineer have offered important help, especially in an area where there is a chance that damp or moist weather may prevent the hay being left out long enough to be in the right condition for bringing in.

The process is known as barn hay-drying, which simply means that the hay is cut, left the minimum time on the field, and then carted into a barn, but it is not an ordinary barn. The floor is of grills up through which comes warm air, which may be produced from electricity, or oil, or any other means, and this produces excellent hay, of an attractive colour, 'flavour', and of high feeding value.

Of course, the equipment to do this again involves the investment of cash in buildings and warm-air production, but often an existing building can be converted cheaply and a simple air-warming system installed—and, of course, it can be used for other crops than hay.

The ordinary way of making hay is to leave it in the sun and air in the swath which is left by the mower, and another machine comes along and turns the grass over so that the air can get through it and more of it is exposed to the sun. There are different makes of these hay tedders which do quickly a job that took a long time by hand and the use of a hay fork.

When the hay has been properly conditioned it is gathered by another machine, a baler, which ties it into bales of about 40 lb and they are carted to the barn for storage until needed to see the stock through the winter.

The making of silage is a very popular form of grass conservation, but it calls for special skills in the management and harvesting of the grass. Its main advantage is that the production of silage is not so dependent on the weather.

The grass is cut, and it must be cut at the right stage of

growth for the best quality of silage, by a machine known as a forage harvester. There are several types, but they do the same job, cutting the grass and pushing it into a blower which blows it into a huge but light trailer with high sides, usually made of wire netting. When the trailer is full the grass is carted to the place where the silage is being made. This may be right into the cattle court already mentioned, where the cows or other cattle may eat it from the pit in the self-feed system already referred to.

The silage may be made in a pit in the field, where cattle may use it when they are out during the winter, or it may be made in a silo for feeding automatically or dug out by a tractor with a forklift.

It will be seen that silage is made from green grass, and it is important to consolidate this grass in the pit so that air does not get into it, as this would spoil it. The consolidation is usually done by running a tractor over it as it is deposited in the pit. There are several ways of keeping the air out once the pit is full—by covering the silage with straw, or by enclosing it in a huge envelope of plastic material.

As hay is light and dry it is easy to handle, but silage is not only solid and heavy when it has been compacted for some time, but also emits an unpleasant smell. On top of this the disposal of the effluent from silage is also a problem. This liquid which comes from the silage pit has become an even more serious problem since legislation came in to prevent pollution of our rivers and streams by 'industrial waste'. Where a farmer has a silage pit which exudes this effluent he must not let it get into a ditch or a stream, no matter how small the stream, as that ditch or stream must at some time find its way to a river, and if there were many farms in one area making silage and letting the smelly liquid seep into even the smallest stream the main river would soon be polluted and the fish killed if there were a high concentration of the liquid. There are several ways in which this liquid can be disposed of, one by making 'lagoons' near the silage pit into which any effluent flows—this applies to some other liquids from the farm, such as the water used with the detergents to clean the dairy cows' stalls or courts—and evaporation of seepage into safe ground away from any stream takes place.

There is seldom a straight cut-and-dried line between hay and silage and between silage and no grazing at all.

Where the farmer is an expert on grassland management he will make a lot of silage and he will also have stock grazing. But they will not just be wandering over any field at will. We have referred in Chapter 8 to the controlled system of grazing for sheep called the forward-creep system. Some farmers will let stock graze early until they can start making silage when the grass is really lush, but the stock on a farm where grassland is intensively used will be strictly controlled, usually by electric fencing which can be moved easily. So a given number of dairy cows are concentrated on a paddock circled by an electric fence, while the rest of the grass fields are being rested or cut for silage. The system is integrated with the stocking rate, the extent and intensiveness of the grassland production, and with the production policy of the farm, not to mention what labour is available or how much capital is available for the provision of the machinery and handling equipment.

It should be mentioned that while silage has the disadvantage of weight and smell and so on, it does lend itself to complete mechanization from cutting to feeding.

Not so many years ago few farmers treated grass as a crop, but more or less as something which 'was there'. Today on many farms, as we have emphasized, grass is a very important crop calling for scientific disciplines and engineering techniques in improving its production and handling and for skill and knowledge on the part of the farmer in the management of his grasslands. A vital factor in intensive grassland production is fertilizer usage, and the scientists who have produced these compound and concentrated fertilizers have made it possible for farmers to produce an impressive quantity of grass from limited areas.

So, as we have said, the plant breeders, the chemists and the engineers among others have all contributed towards the increase in the importance of grass as a crop on the farm, and a whole library of literature on all aspects of grassland production, management, and utilization has grown up—and is still growing.

It is not only on the fertile Lowlands that attention has been increasingly concentrated on grasses and clovers. We have shown that the millions of acres of uplands and the higher hill lands can be the 'reservoir' of the production of the raw materials for our beef and lamb, where the calves and lambs are reared for fattening on the lower ground, or in intensive units already referred to. But on many upland farms the limiting factor in the number of calves that can be kept is how much feed is available to keep them alive through the winters.

Many hill farms have areas of land, heath or poor grazings, which can be improved to produce grass and from that grass make silage for winter keep, and there is an official Government 'Winter Keep' Scheme to encourage this.

One of the examples of this way of increasing beef production from very poor land was provided by the late Mr Joseph Hobbs, of Inverlochy Castle, at the south-west end of the Caledonian Canal, near Fort William. He set about reclaiming by plough-ing and reseeding with grass thousands of acres of this part of Scotland known as 'the Great Glen'. Much of this land had been well kept by crofters, but as Highland farming declined the land went back to the heather and the bracken. But with re-clamation it was made productive again and Mr Hobbs and his staffs made huge tonnages of silage which permitted a tre-mendous increase in the number of cows kept through the winter. Coupled with this big production of silage, he built a number of rough, open concrete shelters into which the cows could go in the very worst weather, and this enabled a herd of up to about 500 breeding cows to be kept on land which carried few cattle and few sheep before this improvement scheme was tackled.

This was called large-scale farming or cattle ranching—the latter term not being very popular with some of the more traditional Highland farmers.

Another highly successful large-scale cattle enterprise is that of Lord Lovat at Beauly Castle on the other side of Inverness-shire. He had a different method. And it was highly successful.

He had a long glen over thirty miles long. At one end near the sea, where his farmlands and better soils were, he kept the cows in winter, hundreds of them, and after their calves were born in the spring he 'trekked' them up to the high ground for the summer. They did only a few miles a day, but they got to the hills, and mothers and calves stayed there, living off the summer grazings as their forebears did in the shielings of old. Meanwhile the grasslands of the Lowland farms were being rested and made productive of fodder to see the cows through the winter on the low ground, with one big difference. Lord Lovat was able to keep his cows *and* calves through this next winter, so he was able to sell the calves at a more mature age in the spring, when the grass was coming and people were looking for cattle to fatten.

So it could be said that grass is the great summer crop, claiming intense interest from farmers and their staffs before they look at the other arable crops on the farm.

CHAPTER II

MARKETING

O NE important summer-time task, already mentioned, is the shearing of the sheep, a job which may be started even before the silage or haymaking is finished. By midsummer the wool on the sheep will be quite long and, while it served well as a protective and warm coat in the winter, it might prove to be too uncomfortably warm in the hot weather, so the sheep are clipped or shorn.

After the sheep have been clipped a colour mark is put on them so that they can be identified, a process especially necessary on the hill farms, where the sheep may become mixed up with other flocks through wandering away from their own areas, although this is not often the cause of a great deal of trouble, as sheep are 'hefted' on to their own hill. The heft is like a policeman's beat which the sheep follow regularly on their round of food-gathering. In fact, this attachment of the sheep to their own ground is so important than when a hill farm is sold the sheep are usually sold with it so that they can stay on the land to which they are acclimatized. A given number of sheep may make up a heft and several hefts make up a hirsel, which is commonly the number of sheep one shepherd looks after. The size of the hirsel will vary with the type of ground, the breed of sheep, and other conditions, but it would normally be around or between 500 and 600 sheep, that is lambing ewes, for once the lambing season is over and before the lambs go away the size of the flock to be managed and looked after is very much enlarged.

An important part of management apart from winter feeding which we have mentioned and the shearing is the protection of the sheep and lambs against many of the ills which beset them. There are many vaccines used against these diseases. In the case of hill sheep many of these diseases are called 'tick-borne' because they are carried by ticks, the little parasites which live on the sheep or in the pastures. Many of our hill lands are infested with these ticks or other parasites, and constant efforts are made by direct vaccination of the animals or the management of the pastures to fight these pests or reduce their effect. One method of management is to bring cattle on to the hill-sheep areas. There is a saying that a sheep's worst enemy is another sheep. One reason for this is that the sheep is a very selective eater, consuming only the best of the grasses and other herbage, which means that eventually the poorer or coarser and less edible grasses may choke out the better varieties on a natural pasture. But cattle eat much coarser vegetation and on top of this trample a lot of this coarse vegetation down and also manure the area. It is a fact that the introduction of cattle on a hill farm, properly managed, could result in an increase in the size of the sheep stock carried.

As we have already seen, much of the shearing is now carried out more under contract and less by neighbours helping out, and the other change here is that the hand shears have given way to electrically operated shears, which speeds up the job in a striking way.

Most of the clipped fleeces are sold unwashed, or in their greasy state, for sheep's wool contains a lot of oil, and from the natural grease in a sheep, lanolin, used in the making of shampoos and as the basis of ointments, is produced.

One important factor affecting the production of sheep for mutton and lamb or wool is the reduction in the area of sheep farming because so much of the land has been taken over for forestry, especially in the uplands.

Farming and forestry are often referred to as the great 'sister' industries, but like many families they have their differences, and very often this controversy arises when sheep farms are being taken over for afforestation. It is a very difficult problem to solve, because we import a much higher proportion of timber and timber products than we do food, but we need food, too.

Just after the Second World War there was a great drive for more afforestation to replace the hundreds of thousands of acres cut down to meet the wartime needs, and while private owners of woodlands were asked to play their part, the main task of expanding our forestlands was carried through by the Forestry Commission, a body created by the Government for the purpose of creating a vast system of state forests. Very often the Forestry Commission was criticized by hill farmers for taking too much land, but today every effort is made to integrate farming and forestry. One answer was to avoid planting an entire hillside, but to leave broad approaches from the bottom of the valley to the top, so that the sheep could use the low ground in the winter and get up to the higher summer pastures when they were available.

There are many cases, of course, where complete farms have been taken over for afforestation simply because many farmers could not make them pay by sheep farming and because the trees could grow on much poorer soil or on steep slopes where farming would be difficult.

Wool is one of the commodities sold by the hill farmer, and this brings us to marketing, which also brings us to one of the biggest basic changes that have taken place in agriculture since man first began to grow his own food rather than live off what grew without any attention from him.

The sheep farmer sells his wool to the Wool Marketing Board, which, it should be remembered, deals only in the fleeces clipped off the live sheep. There is another kind of wool called skin wool, which is pulled by hand off the skins of sheep which have been slaughtered for their mutton and lamb meat, and it is dealt with by specialists called skinners in Scotland and fell-mongers in England. Long ago every little town of any size as well as any large town or city had its skinner's yard where the skins of sheep were processed by taking the wool off them, dividing it up into the different qualities and the skins made into leathers and so on.

In earlier chapters we conjectured as to how early man would have started with his first primitive ideas of trading, with its subsequent evolution to our present-day price review and methods of price-fixing by the Government.

Alongside these guaranteed price systems we have the marketing systems and the marketing systems cover all commodities and not just those which have guaranteed prices. These systems vary widely with different commodities.

Why a Wool Marketing Board or any other board? One thing we must remember is that in spite of progress along many lines of advancement man has retained many of his primitive instincts, and one is to get all he can for himself. At first it was food, but later it was anything from valuables and cash to lands.

But we are concerned with the marketing of farm products and the possible effect of leaving them to be sold by people who still possessed these natural instincts.

During this process of evolution it has come about that, for all practical purposes, as far as food is concerned, we have resolved ourselves into three main classes. There are those who produce it, those who consume it and those, in between, who pass it on. These are the traders who, like the farmers themselves, are in business for a living. In the course of this business they perform a very useful and necessary service in the process of passing the food from the producer to the consumer. It causes resentment, however, whenever there are signs of them trying to dictate in this process or to exploit it. Inevitably, therefore, control is usually necessary in some form or another.

The services which these traders perform for the community include organizing the even flow of foodstuffs, by processing them or packing them or storing them. They are generally known as the distributive trade and they include wholesalers who buy the food in bulk and sell it in smaller quantities to shops who retail it to the public. Most Scotch beef, for instance, goes to the huge fresh meat market at Smithfield in London—it is the biggest market for fresh meat in the world—and the wholesalers who deal in it there have their contacts for the resale of the meat to butchers' shops in London and the Home Counties —the biggest single market for any kind of goods or food in Britain.

The British people have an instinct for freedom in the larger sense, but many of them also see the sense of some discipline for the good of all, and this applies to the marketing of our food. Under the system of a free-for-all the farmer often came off very much second best and this resulted from a natural process.

It was quite natural for a housewife to see if one shop sold cheaper than the next. Sometimes a shopkeeper would cut a price to get her custom and in turn he tried to get a cut rate from the wholesaler, so that when it got back to the producer he often did not get a price which covered the costs of growing, cultivating, and harvesting.

While we speak of controls, much of the trading in the main products of the British farmers is on a basis of freedom, as we saw in the chapter dealing with the Price Review under which most of the commodities get a guaranteed price from the Government while they are sold on the open market and this usually results in the British housewife getting most of her food relatively cheaply—at least compared with the goods sold in many other countries.

One of the biggest faults of the free-for-all system was that often it resulted in oversupply or overdemand and this had a serious effect on prices. At times of oversupply of eggs, for instance, the housewife got them very cheaply, but when there was a shortage on the market it was the retailers or, often to a lesser extent, the poultry farmers who got the benefit of the high prices. So plans were made to see if we could get orderly marketing, which had two beneficial effects—first it evened out the flow of the foods on to the market by trying to avoid gluts and shortages and, second, having done that, the price usually remained stable over the whole year.

Another fault of the market which was not managed in any way at all was that often there was a vast difference between the price the housewife paid and what the farmer got for his produce—a fault that many farmers still think exists to some extent for some commodities.

By the early 1930s the position got so bad that at times farmers poured milk down the drains because it was not worth selling at the price they were offered for it—and sometimes they could get no price at all. These years of the thirties are remembered by older farmers as the years of great depression for British farming, with milk at a few pence per gallon, potatoes at a matter of shillings per ton and sheep too, selling for only shillings per head.

So plans were set afoot to bring some order into this business of marketing farm produce, and milk was one of the first of the products tackled under the first of the Agricultural Marketing Acts passed in 1931. Milk Marketing Boards were set up in England and Scotland and it is well to remember that one of the great architects of these Marketing Acts was the late Colonel Walter Elliot, a great Scottish farmer and legislator who did a vast amount of work getting the legislation through Parliament and also explaining what it meant to the farmers—and the consumers. Although this legislation was designed to help farmers and consumers, some objected very strongly. Naturally a farmer with a good milk round in a big town in the east, say, where not much milk was produced, had no need of a Milk Marketing Board—unlike a farmer in the south-west who could produce milk very easily, but was far from the consuming centres.

The Milk Marketing Boards—Scotland has three, serving the main area of almost half of Scotland from Perth and Argyll to the Borders, the Aberdeen and District Board in the north-east and the North of Scotland Milk Marketing Board based on Inverness—are known as statutory boards because they were created by parliamentary Statute or Act of Parliament.

We need not go into the detail of how the boards work or the differences between them, but they have this basic aim of bringing order and stability in production and in prices—and also, very important, quality of our main foodstuffs.

One of the many ways the Milk Boards brought stability was by building creameries for the making of butter and cheese or milk powder, thus taking the surplus at a time of high production and avoiding a collapse of the market. The Board also regulates the prices between summer and winter production, giving higher prices in winter to avoid an unbalanced market arising from unbalanced production.

The Milk Boards operate the guaranteed-price system on behalf of the Government, and the Potato and Wool Boards do this in much the same way, although their approach to marketing may be a bit different because of the difference in the nature of the commodities. The Potato Marketing Board doesn't have a very easy task, for the people of this country seem to eat roughly the same quantity of potatoes every year, but the yield per acre may vary, so the supply could easily go up or down. A difference of half a ton an acre up or down could affect the supply of potatoes by hundreds of thousands of tons.

There could be oversupply in a good growing year, but the Board do not know what the weather is going to be like. What happens, therefore, is that the acreage is estimated as accurately as possible; then, as the crops start maturing, estimates are made of possible yields, which become more accurate as actual yields are known. Should there be a surplus at one period the Board steps in and buys up quantities of potatoes which are allowed to lie on the farms until the market firms up, or they may be sent away for feed for stock at a reduced price—but remember, this reduced price for a relatively very small quantity of the total output helps to keep the all-over price firm.

As we have shown, most commodities get a guaranteed price from the Government and are sold on the open market. The guaranteed price for potatoes is £14. 10s. per ton and if the average price over Britain falls below that the Government makes up the difference by arrangement with the Potato Board.

The advantages of the stability, quality improvement, and price control these operations provide are obvious. The Potato Board, for instance, has a huge programme of research aimed in several ways—improving quality and yields of potatoes, reducing damage arising from mechanical harvesting and improving the mechanization of the harvesting. Like other boards, it does a lot of demonstrating for housewives in the use of potatoes in various ways, thus helping to expand the market.

Some milk producers, who are known as producer-retailers, sell their milk direct by means of their own milk rounds and not through a Milk Board. All producers, however, share in the market stability brought about by producer-controlled marketing, and therefore the producer-retailers are called upon to pay a small levy to help to maintain a system which ensures this stable market.

All our foodstuffs are sold in the shops without any control of price by the Government—with one exception, milk. The price

Plate 19 *Aberdeen-Angus in Strathspey.* *(Photo Cowper, Perth.)*

Plate 20 *BOCM South Cathkin Halfbred ewe flock in-wintered for feeding trials.*

Plate 21 *Blackface ewes on their native hills in Glenprosen, Angus. (Photo S.A.I. Ltd.)*

Plate 22 *A Cheviot show champion.* (*Photo S.A.I. Ltd.*)

Plate 23 *Suffolk sheep on a Midlothian pasture.* (*Photo S.A.I. Ltd.*)

of milk over the counter is fixed by the Government, because it wished to ensure that this valuable foodstuff should get to the consumers as cheaply as possible, but many farmers feel this last commodity should be freed as well and the Boards given the powers of regulation of prices.

Since the first Boards, for milk, were formed in 1933, others have followed before and after the Second World War, for wool, eggs, and potatoes. Other systems are used or are planned for other commodities. Meat, for instance, is a difficult commodity, because it is in such variety, is so perishable, has such a large proportion of it imported, that a Livestock Commission has been set up to supervise the marketing of livestock and many of the products, but this Commission will not have the close control of, say, the Milk or Potato Boards, but will generally supervise the arrangements for livestock production and marketing, largely through existing channels, but with an interest in improving the marketing organization where it sees improvements can be made.

It will be seen that the powers and control of the various boards and other bodies connected with marketing our home farm produce varies considerably. Many farmers think they should have more powers, especially over imports, for instance. It sometimes happens that imports of foreign potatoes at the wrong time could depress the home market, and farmers feel that something should be done about this.

Again, without going into too much detail, these problems are very thorny ones. As Britain is a great manufacturing and industrial country, we sell manufactures overseas, and often for these we buy food in return or the raw materials for use in our factories. For instance, as we have said, Denmark is a very big customer for our machinery and other manufactures, so Britain guarantees Denmark a share of the bacon market in Britain. Naturally home bacon producers would like to have a bigger share, but the Government must hold the balance between all the interests—not just the farmers'.

There is no doubt that, in spite of many problems, and of the fact that all systems are not perfect, the organization of farm-produce marketing in Britain is envied by farmers in many parts of the world, including the countries across the Channel—but there are still a few highly individualistic farmers who say they do not need marketing boards. They are, however, in an insignificant minority so far as all the main commodities are concerned, for even with some of the defects admitted, few farmers would abandon the present system to enter once again a free-for-all system of disposing of our farm produce.

So that is why, in this sphere of marketing, we have called it one of the great basic changes in farming since man first began to grow food for himself and others. For the individual farmer it has usually meant taking an interest in what happened to his produce after it went through the farm gate.

There is one other aspect of marketing which must be mentioned not only because of its importance but because of its increasing impact on the industry. It may be called co-operation. At first it was in a simple form. Say ten farmers buying each a few tons of fertilizers found that by combining in a big bulk order they obtained the material at substantially lower prices, and this applied to other farming needs. It was only one step from co-operative buying to co-operative selling, and we now have one or two huge organizations engaged in this specialized kind of agricultural trading, some of them handling trade worth millions of pounds a year.

Some of them are general co-operatives, handling all products out and in—supplying the farmer with seeds, fertilizers, tractor fuels, and so on, and buying many of his products for reselling. Some are specialized and there are several examples in Scotland —such as Buchan Meat Producers in the north-east. They buy livestock direct from their farmer members—without the stock going through an auction mart in a live sale—and ship the meat direct through a big agency to the markets in the south, mainly Smithfield, but also to the big cities where the demand is. This farmer-run co-operative deals in meat worth several million pounds a year, and it has also branched out to deal with other commodities.

Another example is Scottish Meat Producers, based on Edinburgh and again doing an increasing annual trade in direct sales from the farm to the wholesale or other outlet. This is known as selling livestock on a deadweight and grade basis as opposed to the liveweight auctions. Many farmers—and butchers—still prefer the liveweight auctions, some farmers because they like to see their stock sold personally and to enjoy, if that is the right word, the interest of taking a gamble on the market, but other farmers prefer the deadweight and grade, which saves them an immense amount of time and trouble by having their stock collected and slaughtered by the group or co-operative of which they are a member, and then paid on the weight and grade which the carcass produces.

By far the majority of farmers still favour the live auctions, but this new interest in deadweight sales has led some of the auctioneering firms to share in the provision of facilities for direct sales on a deadweight and grade basis.

Some of these farmer-run organizations for marketing are impressive in size and some are smaller—some groups got together to sell their young pigs, calves or lambs, or to engage in other forms of direct trading where they think they will have an advantage. For instance, the demand for young calves to be fattened under an intensive system like barley beef has led to the creation of 'calf banks' to ensure a steady flow of supplies of calves to the farms where they will be fattened.

The Government is so keen on farmers helping themselves by these means of co-operative marketing that they have given it special encouragement in the way of grants for setting up co-operatives or for market research to see where agricultural products could best be sold.

One of several examples of this in Scotland concerns the sale of calves from the Western Islands. A scheme was started whereby, instead of going in individual numbers to island or mainland marketing centres, calves were collected, graded by experts and shipped to another organization, a buying one, in the fattening lands of the Lothians.

Another of the many forms of grouping for this sort of co-operative operation is not only in the buying of machinery but in the use of it, whereby, instead of each of three farmers paying about £4,000 for a combine-harvester, maybe five could buy two between them. A problem here is to try to co-operate with farmers who are not far away, but with sufficient difference of climate, soil, or elevation to ensure that they will not all clamour for the machinery at the same time.

In all these changes of moving with the times, the pattern of rural life is changing, too, farmers becoming more businessmen, or men with an interest in the business as well as the purely farming side of farming.

CHAPTER 12

SHOWS AND Y.F.C.

So the pattern of rural life is changing, but, while many of the changes are obvious, and others are underneath the surface or detectable only by an expert, in the larger sense the basic pattern remains, seed-time and harvest, and the summer and winter events that are not directly to do with farming operations, but which loom large on farming calendars—the agricultural shows.

They range from the small local shows, sometimes called 'dykeside' shows from the fact that the animals were often just lined up round the dykes surrounding the ground—to the big regional shows and Scotland's national farm show, the Royal Highland, held in the third week in June.

Scotland is rich in these annual events of high summer or late spring and early autumn. Many of them give a fair picture of the livestock farming in their area, for the basis of most of these shows is livestock. Many shows have been passing through difficult times and some have disappeared, but some have increased in size and strength by sheer determination to get better, and some have increased their size and influence by amalgamation among local societies. As an example of a regional show which decided to strengthen itself we could quote the Royal Northern at Aberdeen, serving a hinterland with some of the best stockmen, especially in beef cattle and sheep, in the country. It is one of the increasing number of regional shows which now has its own permanent site.

Examples of improving shows by amalgamation are the Border Union and Dumfries, each with their own sites, the Border Union on a beautiful park on the banks of the Tweed.

The Northern Counties at Inverness, again a fine regional show, reflecting the stock farming of its area, and Ayr in the south-west, a two-day event and, like the others, serving its area splendidly.

But whatever its size or importance every show is usually the summer highlight of the year in its area. In the early days these shows played a part in improving the livestock of their areas, for only when animals paraded and were compared could breeders see what they could emulate—or avoid. This educational aspect of shows continues, but it, too, is changing, and there is less of an educational aspect in the livestock classes—with some exceptions. The stock at most shows are judged purely on how they look—on conformation, but some classes of some types of stock are going a step further. It is possible at one or two shows to have in the dairy cattle classes where the amount and quality of the milk produced counts for points—this is done only at the bigger shows like the Royal Highland, and in few classes, but it is beginning.

The summer show is often used by the makers of machinery and other needs of the farmer to display the latest of their products. To the two main features of livestock display and the shop window for agriculture's partner industries there is the social side—the meeting of people for a pleasant day out—if the show is lucky with the weather—and the competitive sporting events, with many shows now giving a lot of time and encouragement to show jumping or demonstrations.

Shows vary tremendously in size, but whether they be a small island affair held on the short grassy machair of a Western Isle or a successful regional or county show, such as Perth or the Border Union, or a show that may be little more than a highly successful local fair with animals thrown in, they all manage to offer an amazing variety of attractions. Here breeders meet other breeders, members of the advisory services who help the farmer improve his efficiency are available for consultation, here the makers of machinery and the producers of seeds, feeding-stuffs, fertilizers, or farm books and records have their stands and staffs with a readiness to talk and advise; here a family can have a day out; here a girl may make her first public essay over the fences in a jumping contest or a young farmer take part in a stock-judging or cattle-dressing or sheep-shearing competition—or his sister compete in baking or poultry dressing.

Verily 'there is something for everybody', including especially the townsman and his wife, who are welcome to see this possibly superficial slice of the way of life which provides their beef and eggs and milk and bacon and lamb and beer and whisky.

The animals are divided into breeds and the breeds into classes for different ages and different sexes and the best of the breed after an elimination contest before an expert judge or judges is the champion.

Some shows even have competitions between breeds to find an overall champion, but these interbreed contests create problems of finding judges to adjudicate between breeds, and in the opinion of some are not worth the effort—except perhaps in the case of national dairy shows, where points are awarded for milk production and quality as well as conformation and assessment on looks alone.

In recent years in stock-breeding a new figure has entered the scene, the geneticist, a scientist who is concerned with results only, with the extent to which an animal produces the product, milk, beef, or mutton, which it is destined to do. One such scientist addressing a gathering of 500 Ayrshire cattle breeders was asked by a breeder whether he thought good conformation and a good straight back, etc., were essential in a dairy cow. He replied that if he found a breed of camels with humps on their backs but which produced more milk, then he would breed camels.

But there is no doubt that while new scientific disciplines like genetics, nutritional research, and the science of management are entering more into livestock production, the livestock show did much in the past to improve breeds, and still gives breeders visible comparisons showing how a good bull with the right bloodlines mated to the right strain of cow will bring a calf which should be that little better. The day may come when the only animals allowed into a show are those which have been performance tested—i.e. their milk production recorded in the case of dairy cattle or their weight gain and food conversion catalogued in the case of beef cattle. But these days are still far off and the summer show with its vast variety of attractions will stay a long time.

Many of the shows are, in fact, doing more in a practical educational way with demonstrations of various kinds. The Electricity Authority, for instance, may have a stand showing in life-size machinery or diagrams the latest in electrically controlled environment for poultry or pigs or calves, or in the drying of hay, and the advisory services may have their stands with news of the latest developments in a variety of branches of farming. These advisory services are an important part of agricultural education in the field. Every county in Scotland has its local advisory officers, from the staffs of the agricultural colleges, on general farming, on poultry, on dairying, on beekeeping, etc., but the big industrial firms which service farming in so many ways also have their experts ready and willing to go on to a farm and give their technical advice on a great variety of problems or developments.

These highly qualified experts may be talking to a farmer within sight of a judging ring where a highly expert judge is assessing the bone structure, 'breed character', and main points of an animal that may be an outstanding example of its breed.

Many of the animals on show will have been bred by artificial insemination, a service provided by the Milk Boards, for beef as well as dairy cattle. This A.I. service makes it possible for small farmers to use in their breeding herds bulls of a quality they could not normally afford.

We have already mentioned the national show, the Royal Highland, and since the Highlands form only a small part of Scotland people are curious about why the national show now held in the Lowlands, permanently, should be called the Royal Highland. Towards the end of the eighteenth century a number of landowners met to consider the formation in Edinburgh of a society for the improvement of the Highlands, so in March 1784 'The Highland Society of Edinburgh' held its first general meeting.

Its objectives were very ambitious, including plans for a survey of the Highlands with a view to improving their conditions by the establishment of towns and villages, facilitating communications by roads and bridges, advancing agriculture, and not forgetting a desire to preserve the language, music, and poetry of the Highlands.

The Society did not hold a show until 1822 and this was on a one-acre site at the foot of the Royal Mile which runs from the Castle to the Palace of Holyroodhouse in Edinburgh. It was in what is now the garden of a house and the size contrasts with the 100-acre site of the present show and its 150 acres for car parks and other services surrounding it.

Later it became known as the Highland and Agricultural Society of Scotland and, as its activities extended, shows were held in each of eight different divisions each year, from Inverness to the Borders. In its early days the Society encouraged improvements in farming and stock-breeding by many means, apart from the shows. It got its Royal prefix in 1948. In the years after the Second World War the expense of moving around the country increased alarmingly, and on top of this many of the sites near the larger towns and cities where the show was held were built over for housing schemes or other urban developments. So a decision was made to find a permanent site near the capital where the Society was founded and this site was created on a former golf-course at Ingliston on the western outskirts of the city. It had many advantages, it was flat, accessible, near the airport, a short run from the city and near the end of the approaches to the Forth Road Bridge, which put the show within an hour of a central city like Perth.

Today the show has permanent buildings for meetings and conferences, for accommodating the herdsmen who look after the stock, for the stock themselves, and for many other purposes, including the marketing boards and other organisations such as the Young Farmers.

The Young Farmers' Association, or to give it its proper title, The Scottish Association of Young Farmers' Clubs, is the countryside's own Youth Movement and it plays a vigorous part in the rural life of Scotland. They will be seen taking part in many activities at local shows, holding demonstrations or competitions in summer and discussion meetings in the winter.

Their outlook is far from narrow, as their motto demonstrates: 'Better Farmers, Better Countrymen, Better Citizens'.

The clubs are administered from headquarters in Edinburgh through four areas which have permanent secretaries, and the variety and interest of their activities would take another book to describe fully. Through their discussions and speech-making contests they have given young people the chance to learn to express themselves in public, a valuable asset in modern society; they have a scheme for exchange visits with young farmers from overseas under which the young people come and stay on farms with the families here while the young Scots do the same in the countries they are visiting and this is by no means the end of their international links and effort. The Association provides the secretariat for the Scottish Co-ordinating Committee of the World Assembly of Youth and has direct links with the European Committee for Young Farmers' Clubs.

On the practical level, the Association runs proficiency tests on a huge variety of farm and home crafts, ranging from sheep-shearing to jelly-making. Apart from gaining certificates in the tests, members can aspire to 'Master Craftsman' standard. Over 5,000 boys and girls in the clubs have sat the tests since they started in 1957.

One feature of the clubs' activities is that anyone interested in rural life and work may join, and there are even clubs in one or two of the big cities catering for young people interested in this work, and they include the younger members of the staffs of marts and other firms allied with farming.

The club competitions arouse great interest. They may start at club level or at a county or regional rally and lead right up to international affairs. For instance, there is an international contest for beef-cattle judging. Eliminating contests are held in the areas, and from the finalists a team of three is chosen, and they get a period of coaching from an experienced judge, often one who has been in the team in former years.

The international contest is held at the Royal Highland Show in June and the Scottish team, which has won it several times, will be up against teams from six or seven countries. One year the trophy went as far away as Kansas.

Dairy stock-judging contests on a national level are held also and there are many other national and regional competitions in many farm and farmhouse crafts. The girls play a very big part in these club activities and have their own competitions in, say, dressing poultry for table, jam-making, and baking or dress-making.

In addition to the club and regional and national competitions another important activity is area and national conferences where club and other much wider topics are discussed, often with a keynote address by a prominent national or international figure.

The social side is not neglected, and apart from purely social events for the young people, there are drama presentations and other cultural activities.

Even this brief outline of some of the activities of the Young Farmers' Clubs should make it plain that the movement is vitally important in rural life. One of the many proofs of this is that the highest farming office in Scotland, the Presidency of the National Farmers' Union, which deals direct with the Government on matters of farming policy, has often been held by men who made their first public speech in a Young Farmers' Club.

Another very important institution of Scottish rural life is the Scottish Women's Rural Institute, which has done a great deal to provide interest and instruction to thousands of its members throughout the countryside.

In spite of the advent of television and other distractions which have had the effect of changing the pattern of life in the countryside, 'The Rural', as it has been affectionately called, has carried on with activities too varied to begin to list them.

They have their meetings for discussions, talks, demonstrations, and the development of such activities as floral art in the winter months, and at many of the summer shows the Institute's members are the backbone of support for the baking and home crafts sections.

CHAPTER 13

THE BREEDS OF CATTLE

W E have made it clear that Scottish farming is based on livestock and livestock products, as about 80 per cent of the annual value of Scottish farm produce comes from livestock and the rest from crops.

It therefore follows that a great deal of attention and expertise is devoted to the production of livestock of a high quality. The stock may be divided into two categories, the pedigree and the commercial, although there may be many pedigree animals in commercial herds, especially dairy herds. But there are the *élite* pedigree herds of beef cattle which in turn provide the sires for the commercial beef herds. These *élite* herds strive to maintain the highest possible quality in production and fertility.

It is very doubtful if any country of its size in the world can equal Scotland's fame in the production of pedigree cattle. Some people prefer the word 'pure-bred' to pedigree, as pure-bred means any animal that has no blood of any other breed in it, and it may be quite a commercial type, while pedigree is often taken to mean an animal which is acceptable for registration in the herd book of a breed society.

The most famous of the Scottish breeds of beef cattle is the Aberdeen-Angus, an all-black polled or hornless breed which was developed from the local breeds of the counties of Aberdeen and Angus. The local black, and sometimes red, cattle were known centuries ago, but the first 'improver' was Hugh Watson of Keillor, near Coupar-Angus, who founded a herd in 1808 and used the local types to 'fix' a breed which was consistent in appearance, quality, and commercial value. Other pioneers followed him and it was not long before the breed was winning honours far beyond its native area.

The Aberdeen-Angus is not so large as other beef breeds such as the Shorthorn or the Hereford. It is small, compact, is early maturing, has a low percentage of bone to flesh, and produces beef of outstanding quality. There are herds all over Britain now and in every country where good beef cattle are appreciated, such as many Commonwealth countries, the United States of America, and the Argentine.

Historically the Beef Shorthorn is older than the Aberdeen-Angus. Records show that it was developed from a local breed in Durham and the surrounding region where selective breeding was practised as far back as 1750. In the case of the Beef Shorthorn the pioneer was Amos Cruickshank of Sittyton, Aberdeenshire, and he and those who followed created a world-wide breed which brought buyers from all over the globe to the great annual sales for which Perth is the main centre.

Another Scottish beef breed is the Galloway, a hardy hill animal very like the Aberdeen-Angus at first glance, as it is black and hornless, but its coat tends to be more curly, and it is not only black, for dun-coloured animals are also registered in the herd book.

The Galloway gets its name from its native area in the southwest of Scotland, where for many years it was almost completely confined, but in the last decade or two this hardy hill breed has expanded dramatically not only in the United Kingdom but overseas.

The fourth beef breed is the Highland, the long-horned, shaggy-coated cattle of the Western Highlands and Islands, rather slower maturing than the other breeds, but one which plays its part. In fact, they all play their part in helping beef producers to use all the varied types of land in Scotland to produce high-quality beef.

We could give many examples of how these breeds are used to produce beef from the pure-bred animal, or from the crossing of different breeds. For instance, a Beef Shorthorn bull is mated with a Highland cow and this produces a heavier faster-maturing cross which can be fattened further down the hill, or the females from this cross could in turn be mated with an Aberdeen-Angus to produce an even more compact, faster-maturing animal which could fatten more quickly on the better lands.

The Galloway, crossed with a white Shorthorn—the Shorthorns come in three colours, red, roan, and white—produced the famous 'blue-grey', one of the foundations of the beef stock in many part of Scotland.

Two other Scottish beef breeds must be mentioned. The Belted Galloway is a small breed in numbers. It has a wide white belt round its black body and is one of the most distinctive cattle breeds in Britain, and has it enthusiastic followers.

Then there is the newest beef breed of all, first launched in public in 1966 after seventeen years of hard experimental work on a Western Island, the Island of Luing off the coast near Oban, by three brothers, Denis, Shane, and Ralph Cadzow, who have big farming interests in the arable Lothians and Borders.

Their aim was to cross the Beef Shorthorn with the Highland, with a preponderance of the Shorthorn, and produce a new commercial breed which would live in these same areas, but mature faster and also cut out the need for keeping a Highland herd in order to produce the Shorthorn-Highland cross. In other words, this Luing breed, to give it the name it has taken from its native island, cuts out one step in the process of breeding beef in this area by fixing a Shorthorn-Highland cross which reproduces itself.

It is just beginning to expand and it is too early to say what it will do, but it has made a promising start.

The Hereford is not a native Scottish breed, but it has made great headway in Scotland since the early 1950s. It is a big beefy animal and a good ranger, and it is useful as a crossing sire on other breeds, including the native Ayrshire dairy breed, for producing beef from the dairy herd which we shall come to in a moment.

Also in use in Scotland are numbers of Lincoln Reds and Red Polls from over the Border, whose presence shows that Scottish breeders are enterprising in their experimentation with other native breeds. There are also a number of the hardy Welsh Blacks, but the traditional beef-cattle production systems are based on the Aberdeen-Angus, Beef Shorthorns, and Galloways, and the Highland cattle and their crosses.

Note, we say 'traditional beef-cattle production systems',

because this is very important when considering beef production in Scotland. What is known as the best Scotch beef which earns a better price in Smithfield markets and other big centres comes from cattle bred for beef, but the nation needs much more beef than we can produce from our breeds which are bred purely for beef, so we have this policy for producing beef from dairy cattle, already outlined, where a dairy farmer may mate some of his dairy cows with a beef bull, Shorthorn, or Hereford, and sometimes Aberdeen-Angus.

There are also breeds of cattle which are known as dual-purpose in that they have a good milk output, but also produce good beef, or at least certain strains of them do. The biggest and most numerous breed which comes into this category is the British Friesian, which originated in Holland. It is a dairy breed really, but any calves not wanted for dairy herd replacements, especially the steers, can be fattened for beef production, even without being the progeny of a beef bull and a Friesian mother.

The Friesian gives very large quantities of milk compared with other breeds, although it is not usually so rich as say the Ayrshire milk, but the Friesian breeders, by using scientific testing and breeding methods, have been improving the milk quality of the breed in recent years.

Because so many Friesian calves can be fattened for beef without being the product of a beef cross, they are in great demand for production of beef by intensive methods such as 'barley beef', which we have already discussed.

Many farmers, even in some of the traditional beef areas, are turning to Friesians for beef production, because of the large and steady supply of calves and their relative cheapness, but there has been such a demand for Friesian calves that the price has gone high enough to make farmers interested in beef from the dairy herd look to other sources and many are turning to the native dairy breed, the Ayrshire.

The Ayrshire is really the only dairy breed native to the British Isles, as the Friesians are not originally British and the Jerseys and Guernseys are from the Channel Islands, while the Dairy Shorthorn, which used to have a great popularity in

England, especially the North, is a dual-purpose breed.

This urge to get more beef from dairy herds has led to investigation of the Ayrshire as a possible source. It was found that mating a Beef Shorthorn bull or a Hereford for some strains provided a good beef calf, especially the Shorthorn cross, but it was found that with the right management straight Ayrshire steer calves could be brought on for beef and the Ayrshire has been playing this dual role to an increasing extent.

We have compared the Friesian and Ayrshire as milk producers and perhaps we should enlarge on this. The efficiency of a dairy cow is judged on the quantity and quality of the milk it produces and we have said the Friesian is a high producer, while the Ayrshire may not have the same high average, but gives a little better quality.

Milk quality is measured chiefly by the percentage of butter fat and the non-fatty solids in it and the dairy farmers are paid on a sliding scale for the quality of milk measured in these terms.

The Friesians have the advantage of giving heavy milkings, but not such creamy milk, and it is claimed for the Ayrshires that apart from the quality—as well as the substantial quantity of milk they produce—they are also better at converting food into milk than some other breeds.

Apart from the quality of the milk itself, it must be produced under hygienic conditions as laid down by the Milk and Dairies Acts. A farmer can lose his right to produce milk not only for producing milk below the standards for butter fat, but also for producing milk under unhygienic conditions, so building and equipment and methods are inspected, and the milk sampled.

All this is a great contribution to the health of the public, the consumers who drink the milk.

As the milk is paid for on its compositional quality, it can be understood that farmers try to improve the breeding of their herds to attain improvement in the composition of the milk.

While the Ayrshire and the Friesian are the main breeds of milk cattle in Scotland there are also a number of very good herds of the Channel Islands breed, the Jerseys, while a few Guernseys may be seen. The Jerseys have quite a strong follow-

Plate 24 *This Blackface ram was champion at the show where he was entered.* (Photo S.A.I. Ltd.)

Plate 25 *Wessex Saddleback sow and her litter. (Photo S.A.I. Ltd.)*

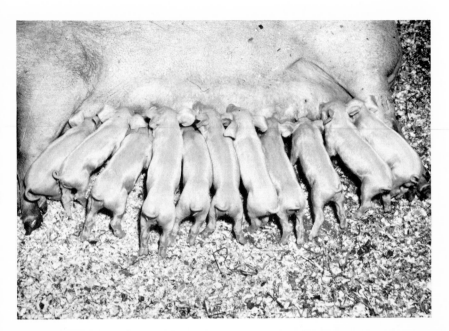

Plate 26 *Feeding time in the piggery when a litter get their daily nourishment from the mother sow.* (*Photo S.A.I. Ltd.*)

Plate 27 *'Broiler' is the popular name given to chickens fed and reared intensively for the table, and the interior of a typical broiler 'house' is shown above. Some broiler houses hold up to* 30,000 *birds at one time.*

Plate 28 *Tiers of battery hens in a big egg-producing unit in Aberdeenshire. Note how the eggs roll out for easy collection.*

ing in Scotland and have their own classes at the Royal Highland and some other shows.

The Jerseys are most attractive little animals and give very rich creamy milk and, contrary to some beliefs, they are not at all delicate animals and may be found in many parts of Scotland, including the northern areas around Inverness.

While the name of Scotch beef was made by animals bred for beef, especially the Aberdeen-Angus, the Beef Shorthorn and the Galloway, it has to be borne in mind that about three-quarters of the beef produced at home comes as a by-product of the dairy herd. The 'traditional' Scottish beef producers and those people in the south who appreciate the richly flavoured, tender steaks of the Angus and the other beef breeds and crosses may turn up their noses at 'dairy beef', but this dairy beef is quite acceptable in many of the big industrial centres where often the housewives like the lean meat without any fat. The connoisseurs of beef know that it is the fat that gives the beef its rich flavour, especially when the fat is marbled through the lean, and this 'marbling' is looked for by the butcher who sells the highest quality. When this marbled beef is cooked the fat melts away and leaves the succulent flesh, richly flavoured.

One of the reasons why dairy beef gets a good market is that apart from the fact that properly fed dairy beef can be quite tasty, it has not much fat on it, and it is lean which attracts many housewives, who think fat is nothing but a waste, as they are more interested in lean-ness than richness of flavour. Of course, when it comes to 'manufacturing' beef—for pies, sausages, and similar types of product—the very high standards of flavour are not so important.

This richly flavoured superlative Scotch beef is recognized by getting a higher price in the big markets like Smithfield, but many farmers think that the extra cost of producing it is often not covered by the extra price. This has not meant that many are going out of beef production, but it has meant that more are trying ways of producing the same high quality by more economical means.

Some of the big buyers in Smithfield buy direct from Scottish farmers whose product they know, and one of the biggest quality meat chain of shops in London and the home counties have their own buyers in the north-east and north of Scotland, where they have over many years established links with the quality beef producers whose product they know.

The biggest single beef-producing farmers' co-operative is Buchan Meat Producers, with headquarters in Peterhead in the northeast of Aberdeenshire, and its direct purchases of cattle, sheep, and pigs on a deadweight basis runs into several million pounds a year, with direct transport to Smithfield and other centres of consumption.

CHAPTER 14

THE BREEDS OF SHEEP

IN looking at the different breeds of cattle we have seen that these specialized breeds and their crosses fulfil special purposes, and especially the purpose of making the best use of the type of land on which they live, whether it be on the hills or the fertile lowlands.

If this is true of the cattle, it is even more true of the sheep, where over many years breeds and crosses have been developed to suit the terrain—or certain kinds of management—but all with the end aim of meeting the demand for a product which the consumers need.

And it is a fact that changes occur in the kind of meat which the consumers want. For instance, many years ago the flocks of sheep kept on the hills were wethers, castrated male sheep, which were allowed to mature for two or three years, and their meat was mutton, but today the demand is for lamb, so the flocks kept are ewes, which produce the lambs for the market and, in the case of some of the ewe lambs, for flock replacement.

Scotland has two breeds of mountain sheep, the Blackface and the Cheviot. The Cheviot is subdivided into two breeds which we shall consider later. The Blackface is considered the most numerous sheep breed in Britain, and thousands of them live on the hills and the moorlands and other areas covered by the term rough grazings. Although it is called the Blackface, the faces of all these sheep are not black. Many have black and white markings on their faces, but blackfaced or black-and-white-faced, the hardy long-wooled breed has thoroughly established itself over huge areas of hills and uplands.

In an earlier chapter we told how the sheep took over from the cattle as a source of income for the landowners and led to the situation known as 'The Clearances', whereby many inhabitants of the hills and glens were cleared, often forcibly, from the land in order to make room for great sheep farms.

Incidentally the term for a Blackface with white patches is 'brockit'.

The Blackface is a small, active, and very hardy animal, and this hardiness has caused it to be used in other lands than the hills and moors of Scotland. Many flocks of Blackfaces may now be found in places like Dartmoor in the south-west of England and on some of the high cold, Yorkshire wolds. It is a horned breed and the horns of the rams are very large, thick, and curly.

The fleece is not heavy, about 4 lb to 5 lb, and it is in great demand for the mattress trade, with large exports to places like Italy.

Although it is not true in every respect, it may be said that the Blackfaces cover the heather-clad hills while the Cheviots cover the green or grassy hills like the hills of their native Border country. On the very high hills the Blackfaces are bred pure, but lower down they are crossed with the Border Leicester ram to produce the Greyface—another example of using crossing to produce a heavier animal from a light hill one.

We have already mentioned that the young female sheep, the ewe hoggs, are usually wintered away for their first winter, before they go on to the hills to produce several crops of lambs.

We mentioned in the case of dairy cattle that inside any one breed there could be different strains. Scientists dealing with living things call this 'variations within the species', and we have this in the Blackface sheep. Over the years breeders worked to improve the types, either to suit certain types of ground or weather or for the economic production of meat. So with the Blackface we have three distinct types and they are known as the Newton Stewart, Lanark, and Perth types. They take their names from the areas where they have their main sales, although Stirling may be said to come in as a big centre for the Perth type. These types vary in wool quality, length, and in other ways, but it would sometimes take an expert to distinguish between them, unless the specimens were extreme examples of each type, for the three strains are often interbred to bring about a desired result.

The other main mountain breed, the Cheviot, which takes its name from the Cheviot Hills of the Border country between Scotland and England, is a white-wooled breed and there are two distinct types, the South Country Cheviot and the North Country Cheviot, although some breeders prefer to know them as the Cheviot and North Country Cheviot. The original or Border Cheviot lives, as we have said, on the lower or grassy hills, but there are some Cheviot flocks which are kept on the lower ground and are known as parkland flocks. The North Country Cheviot was developed from Cheviot sheep brought to Caithness by Sir John Sinclair at the end of the eighteenth century and they are a much bigger sheep than the original breed. Both types of Cheviot are to be found in other parts of Scotland than the Borders and the north, but their largest numbers are to be found in the areas where they originated or were developed.

Again, as in the case of the Blackfaces, we have a cross with the Cheviot for the purpose of using a hill breed to produce a cross for use on lower ground. When a Cheviot ewe is crossed with a Border Leicester ram it produces the Halfbred which is a very popular sheep for keeping on lower ground farms. Many of these low-ground farms keep flocks of Halfbred ewes to produce the lambs which go to the butchers. Very often these Halfbred ewes are crossed with Oxford Down or Suffolk Down rams to produce Down Cross Lambs, which fatten quickly, produce the small joints which the modern housewife likes and have flavour and colour in their meat.

So we can have Cheviots, bred pure on the hills, or in some cases in parkland flocks, crossed with Border Leicester rams to produce Halfbreds and these Halfbreds in turn produce the Down crosses. These Halfbred ewes are in great demand south of the Border and English farmers come up to the Border sales and buy them in large numbers. Perhaps it is necessary to say that in recent years the Oxford Down has become less popular as a crossing ram, as it is a big breed, and with the demand for small compact lambs for the market the Suffolk and some other of the English Down breeds, like the Hampshire or Dorset, are becoming popular in Scotland. Not all of these Down breeds are used for crossing, some going to market pure, as there is a demand for them, too.

It is a criticism of the British sheep industry that we have too many breeds and that until we can get much more uniformity in the lambs produced British farmers cannot compete with countries like New Zealand, which are famous for a high-quality, very uniform type of lamb. In fact, it has been said that New Zealand lamb is the only product which many London butchers will order from Smithfield over the telephone, as they are so sure of the uniformity of the grades, whereas in so many other cases the variation is such that they want to see the carcasses.

One big advantage the home sheep producers have is that their product is sold fresh, and it is quite an advantage over imported frozen lamb.

Movements have started to improve the 'image' of Scotch lamb by grading quality carcasses, so that a buyer will have a surer idea that when he orders Scotch lamb of a given type he will be reasonably sure of getting it. This does not mean that up till now the lamb has been of varied quality and type. There are several big agencies buying direct, as in the case of cattle, slaughtering and selling direct to markets lambs which are recognized and appreciated by the trade and its customers. A grading scheme should make the sale of quality lamb a sale of a recognized quality product, a product with a brand or some kind of guarantee that the quality is high, level, and does not vary.

The Border Leicester was developed in Scotland from an English breed and, as we have already seen, its chief use is for crossing with the Blackface or Cheviots to produce Greyfaces or Halfbreds.

The Border Leicester is a white-wooled hornless breed and has high-quality wool like the Cheviot. The Border Leicester and its progeny fatten quickly. Another advantage is that when well looked after the flocks have a high lambing percentage, up to 170 lambs per 100 ewes. It is in use in many parts of Scotland, England, and Ireland, and probably has the highest export reputation of any of our native sheep breeds.

In recent years from an area of Northumberland another

variation of the breed, the Blueheaded Leicester, has come over the Border into Scotland. It is gaining popularity among some commercial sheep producers for crossing.

The Border Leicester has found popularity also in Wales, where the rams are used to produce the Welsh Halfbred.

In other words, the Border Leicester is known as an 'improver', and this is actually the name given to Scotland's newest breed of sheep. It was produced after several years of experiment by Mr Brian Cadzow at Glendevon, a few miles west of Edinburgh. The Improver is a product of a highly complex experiment of cross-breeding, using several Continental breeds from Finland, France, and Germany along with some home breeds. For instance, the Finnish breed used is very prolific, and have 'litters' of lambs rather than even the twins or triplets which are thought to be unusual in our own breeds, while the French breed was used for its ability to produce a lot of milk and so on, other blood being infused into the breed for other reasons. These other reasons included quick maturing and heavy fleshing.

Quite apart from this achievement in producing a new breed, Mr Cadzow did something equally interesting. He created a new system of intensive sheep breeding by getting flocks to produce crops of lambs closely after each other and indoors. The production of sheep indoors released former pastureland for the production of the more valuable cash crop, barley.

Here is one modern example of the men who were the first improvers of the native breeds of livestock, the men who created the breeds of cattle, sheep and pigs—not forgetting horses— from the native varieties that we know today and which led to the claim that Britain is 'The Stud Farm of the World'.

While the Blackface, the Cheviot, and the Border Leicester are the main native Scottish breeds—with the new-comer, the Improver—we have shown that many of the Down breeds have a solid and in some cases increasing hold on the Scottish sheep industry, and mention of the Oxford Down, South Down, Hampshire Down, Dorset Down, Suffolk, and others does not complete the list, as there are examples of the Welsh Mountain and Romney Marsh breeds to be found north of the Border.

There is one other native and very interesting breed, the Shetland, from the most northerly of the Northern Isles. It is a small breed, and this is true both in numbers and in size. Its flesh is not very plentiful, and it does not mature very fast, but when well managed and fed the flavour and texture of the flesh is excellent. The Shetland sheep come in different colours, black, grey, or brown (these brown sheep are known locally as 'moorit'), and white.

The Shetland produces very fine wool which commands very high prices and is used for the production of the world-famous Shetland knitwear. Incidentally the Shetland sheep are not clipped. The loose wool is pulled off by hand and sorted very carefully for use in the making of Shetland shawls.

As the skilled breeders developed the breeds and their crosses over the years to meet the demands of the big markets in the south, so the skills of the flockmasters and the shepherds increased, but many people fear that this in itself is not enough, for in an earlier chapter we mentioned the efforts to bring more intensive methods into the sheep industry in order to improve the returns to the farmers. So new methods of management, like the creep feeding already referred to, and intensive methods of producing lambs indoors are being tried.

Sheep produce three sources of income for the farmer, mutton and lamb, wool and store lambs. The importance of each commodity in the economy of a particular farm will depend on where that farm is situated. For instance, a farm high in the Highlands will produce lambs which will be sold as stores for someone else to fatten. Therefore, on such a farm store lambs and wool will be the important commodities. On the lowland farm, which produces fat lamb and mutton, wool will not be so important.

Many hill farmers, especially those who cannot fatten their lambs, but must sell them to others to do this, are at a disadvantage in that they sell only one commodity which gets the guaranteed price we mentioned when we were dealing with the Price Review system. That commodity is wool. There is a guaranteed price for mutton and lamb, but it goes to the producer of the fat lambs and sheep.

For these reasons Highland and Island farmers depend very much on the sales of store lambs or of the cast ewes which are sold off because they have finished their lives on the hills. It is possible for a farmer on the Island of Mull, which has a very big sheep population, to take his sheep and lambs to the mainland to a sale where the prices may be very poor indeed, but it would not pay him to ship them all the way back, so he will have to let them go at prices which will not pay him, and when this happens for one or two years in succession, as it has on occasion, the hill-sheep industry can become very depressed.

One answer is that many of these sheep farms can be turned into forests, for the country imports a very large percentage of its needs of timber and timber products, but we need food, too, and there is always this problem of balancing the demands of farming and forestry when it comes to land use in the hills and moorlands and islands.

In one really bad depression some hill farmers claimed that they made more profit off the hares and the deer that they shot on their hill farms than from the sheep.

In the chapter on the Price Review we mentioned that the Government gave guaranteed prices for most of the main commodities produced by British farmers in order to encourage production of as much food as possible from our own fields and to save us spending money on food from overseas. This is one form of agricultural support. As we have pointed out, apart from wool the hill farmers do not produce commodities which get the guaranteed prices, so there are other forms of direct assistance to encourage farmers to keep the sheep and the cattle on the hills and provide the material for the farmers to fatten on the low ground.

There are hill-cattle and hill-sheep subsidies, and special grants for fencing, drainage, and land improvement or reclamation.

A hill farmer will get a fixed sum, say £1 for every ewe which is on the hill, or £17 for a cow, and for every calf produced another fixed sum.

An argument arises here between the two types of farmer—those who produce the store stock, lambs and calves and those who fatten them. The men who fatten the stock, known as the feeders, claim that there should be higher guaranteed prices for their fat lambs and beef cattle. Their argument is that a good price for the end-product will mean a bigger demand and therefore a better price to the hill farmers for their store stock. But the hill men think there should be more direct help and encouragement for them to keep the hills stocked, so they suggest that, especially in a year of disastrous prices, they should get a substantial increase in these grants, which are known as production grants, as their aim is to encourage production from these lands.

As these grants are paid by the taxpayer, the Government must hold the balance between the farmers who produce the food and the consumers who eat it. But it must always be remembered that this system of agricultural guarantees and support does have the effect of keeping prices of food in Britain well below the average for the same types of food in almost all the other industrialized countries of the world. In fact, farmers will say that these subsidies are not 'farmers' subsidies' at all but consumer subsidies. They can point to several months in a recent year when the price of beef was so high that it was above the Government's guaranteed prices, so there was no need to pay the farmer any subsidy at all—but the housewives complained bitterly at the high price of beef.

Another point is that if as a result of farm subsidies the price of food is kept reasonable, everybody, including poorer people and old-age pensioners, gets the advantage, whereas if the prices were high—which means the farmers would need less subsidies—some people just could not afford some foods at all.

CHAPTER 15

PIGS AND POULTRY

W E have devoted special chapters to cattle and sheep, but there are two more species of livestock which are important in farming, although they have now come into more specialized production processes—pigs and poultry.

In an earlier chapter we indicated that the production of pigs was not so seasonal as the other main types of stock, when we said that the bacon which appeared on the breakfast table every day was one of the daily 'harvests' like the milk which went on all the year round.

The production of pigs and pig-meat in the shape of pork and bacon is an important sector of farming, and perhaps it has seen more changes than any other type of stock with the exception of poultry, at which we shall be looking in a moment or two. We have seen that many types of dairy cows produce meat as well as milk and that sheep produce wool as well as meat, but the pig is kept for only one product—meat. This meat will be either pork or bacon and each of these products will demand a different kind of pig. For the production of pork it is desirable to have a pig that will become plump and carry meat while it is still young. This is known as early maturity. A pig will usually reach this stage when it is ready to be killed for pork at about fourteen to sixteen weeks.

The bacon pig, however, is expected to yield a larger quantity of meat which will be lean and suitable for nice rashers of bacon when cured, without too much fat.

The ideal bacon pig, therefore, will be long and quite lean and will reach maturity in five or six months.

The two main breeds of pig used in Scotland are the Large White and the Landrace, although there are a number of coloured pigs in use like the Essex and Wessex Saddlebacks, which are blue-black-coloured pigs with heavy white markings.

As in the production of beef and lamb, there is some cross-breeding, but in the main the breeds are produced pure for whatever the end-product is to be—pork or bacon. As we have seen earlier, there is in pigs, as in so many other living things, what we have already called 'variations within the species', which means that some strains of one breed will be good for one purpose and other strains for another purpose.

There is one important difference between pig production in Scotland and pig production in England and Wales, and it is that by far the largest percentage of pig-meat produced in Scotland is for bacon, while in England and Wales a far larger proportion of the pig herds produce pork. It seems that the people of Scotland are not very great pork-eaters and efforts have been made to increase the popularity of pork as a dish north of the Border.

As the main breeds for bacon production are the Large White and the Landrace, we will look at them. In Britain there are about twelve recognized breeds of pigs. We have already mentioned the Essex and the Wessex Saddleback, but there are many others like the Welsh which have a big hold on pig production in England as well as in Wales, and there are other breeds with the delightful names of Gloucester Old Spots and the Long White Lop-eared. There are still commercial breeders who like to cross the Large White with the Wessex or Essex, but this practice in Scotland is not so general as it was.

The Large White is sometimes known as the Yorkshire and, in fact, in the United States of America the name Yorkshire is retained by the organization which looks after the interests of the breed. It got its original name because it originated in Yorkshire and, like all other breeds of stock, this breed, too, had its improvers until we have the breed as it is today—and efforts are still being made further to improve its performance.

There are dual-purpose pigs as well as cattle, some providing animals which could go for pork or bacon and some better for one or the other. The Large White is mainly a bacon pig, and it is the most numerous breed in Britain, with a big interest in overseas countries to which it has been exported, especially to Canada and America.

Unlike some other breeds whose ears are rather floppy and are called lop-eared, the ears of the Large White are rigid, and this is taken as a sign that the breed is less docile than some other breeds which are lop-eared. In fact, Large Whites are not quite so docile as others. This can be an important consideration when the time comes for the sows to farrow, or have their litters.

When a sow goes out into the field to graze it is usual to put a ring in her nose. Otherwise she will root up the turf and damage the grass, because it is the pig's natural instinct to dig for worms, grubs, and roots.

A gilt, as the young female is called, gives birth to her first litter when she is about a year old and thereafter, with right management, has two litters every year. A good sow can be expected to have ten or a dozen piglets in each litter, which will mean more than twenty piglets every year. If half of these are females, it will be easily seen that in pigs any farmer who wishes to increase output very quickly can do so, and this can cause problems in pig production. When prices are poor farmers give up pigs, but when they go higher more farmers go in for pigs, and very soon there are too many for the market to absorb and the prices come down again. This fluctuation in numbers and profitability is one of the problems of the pig industry, so the Government has taken steps to try to control it to some extent by linking the guaranteed price for pigs to a given pig population. So, if pig numbers rocket up above this stated number the guaranteed price comes down and this discourages more production. This does not solve the problem completely, but it helps.

The sow suckles the piglets until they are eight weeks old and then they are taken from their mothers, which is known as weaning. At this stage the piglets are called weaners and this is when they are either kept for fattening on their own farm or sold to other farmers to fatten.

For some farmers their main income from pigs is the sale of these weaners and in some parts of the country farmers producing weaners have formed themselves into groups for the sale of these young pigs, just as has been done in calves for the production of beef by any of the intensive methods. This type of co-operation is of benefit to the buyers as well as the sellers, as there is a co-ordination in the selling and the buyers are assured of steady supplies in the numbers they want.

Many farmers keep a small number of sows and some quite a large number as part of the other enterprises on the farm, but some farmers specialize in pig production alone and some of these are on quite a large scale with long rows of houses in which the sows live and in which their progeny are fattened when they are weaned.

Because of the fertility of the sows and the frequency of their production of litters, the pig lends itself to systems of intensive production and for the large-scale pig producers this is indeed a very highly specialized business.

The pig industry is another branch of farming into which a great deal of scientific research has gone with the aim of improving the production and efficiency and therefore the income of the producers. Because of the speed with which numbers can be produced there can be speedier results from the scientific disciplines used to improve the efficiency of the pig— as a converter of food and a producer of the right type of conformation for, say, bacon.

These efforts to get breed improvement were being made by the breeders themselves by breeding from strains which brought improved results, but this was on a very small scale. Then one of the big feeding-stuffs firms started a scheme for the testing of boars at a central point. A breeder could send in two pigs from a litter produced by a boar and all these pigs from many different boars were housed and managed and fed in exactly the same way, so that their performance could be measured— in the conversion of their feed into meat, in the rate at which they gained weight and in their conformation, and in other characteristics such as general health. In other words the performance of the progeny decided the fate of their sire—just as we saw in the performance tests of dairy cattle. Boars which produced pigs of poor performance were slaughtered, so that gradually breeding is being concentrated on the better boars.

Some years ago this system of testing boars was put on a national basis by a new body, the Pig Industry Development

Authority, set up by the Government to bring about improvements in the pig industry in this and in other ways.

This is just one example of how British livestock producers—in this case pig producers—are working towards improvement of their industry, and geneticists, nutrition experts, recorders, engineers and architects, and many others are taking part in this kind of work, from trying to find the best strains and the most effective way of feeding them to seeing what is the best and most efficient type of housing, some of which will have completely automatic feeding systems installed.

In years gone by the farmer would have killed his own pig and cured it or smoked it himself, or his wife would have done it, and a cured side or haunch could be seen hanging from the rafters, a much more common sight in England, perhaps, than in Scotland, where, for instance, the Highlander had a superstition against pigs.

But today farmers' wives will buy their bacon from a grocer, who gets it from a bacon factory, ready packed in an attractive package with the brand name of the curer on it.

Because of this much higher production of bacon than pork in Scotland, the bacon factory is an important adjunct to pig production here. And Scotland has some big and well-known factories which have huge numbers of pigs going through them every week. The most common system is for a pig farmer to make a contract with the factory to supply a given number of pigs at regular intervals, again a system that is of benefit to both, for the farmer knows what he is going to get for his pigs and the factory has a steady supply—which is very important in this kind of business, where irregularity of supply would lead to breaks in production and uneconomic working.

This pressure to improve the performance of the pigs more and more has added to the farmer's need for skilled management, feeding, and recording the performance of his pigs, but the time taken in this work is valuable, for the farmer who keeps such records can tell at once whether certain pigs are not reaching the desired performance, in which case he will look again at his breeding programme.

Only a small percentage of the boars living on our farms are tested, but their number is increasing and so are their progeny, so while a farmer may not have a tested boar on his farm he might have a boar by a boar which has gone through the test. But when he goes to a sale of pedigree pigs from which he wishes to buy breeding stock, gilts or boars, he can still see in the catalogue a lot of information which can be of help to him in buying. Let us say a boar is listed in the catalogue at the sale on the farm where these pigs are bred. The buyer will be able to see the average size of litter produced in this boar's family, or by the mother of the gilt which he is considering buying. The actual size of the litter is not the only important thing. The other is how many were brought to the weaning stage, as some piglets die before this stage is reached. Also on the catalogue there will be listed the grading achievements of this family of pigs when pigs from it were sent to the bacon factory for slaughter. Some families of pigs achieve a consistently high grading at the bacon factory, so, understandably, buyers will be willing to pay more. There are three kinds of sales of pedigree stock: the draft sale at the farm where the stock is bred and so all the pigs are from this one herd; the collective sale held at a selling centre where different breeders send in their pigs for sale (this sale is usually preceded by a show, so that the show champion usually makes a good price at the sale); and more recently these official boar-testing stations we have mentioned have also had sales of tested boars.

Very often at the bigger collective sales there are also bacon-carcass competitions, where pig producers may enter carcasses for showing and providing another comparison between their produce and that of others. All the pigs entered for a carcass competition are put through a bacon factory, and there the sides hung up in a hall of the auction mart where the live pigs are being sold. An expert judges them and, again, the breeder who can produce a champion carcass will find that his reputation is further increased, and so he would hope that when he comes to sell his breeding pigs people will remember this and pay that little extra.

Because of the speed with which they can be reproduced, pigs can in times of scarcity and high prices of other meats help to

Plate 29 *An Aberdeenshire plant where thousands of chickens are plucked, cleaned and packed for transport to the sales centres. (Photo S.A.I. Ltd.)*

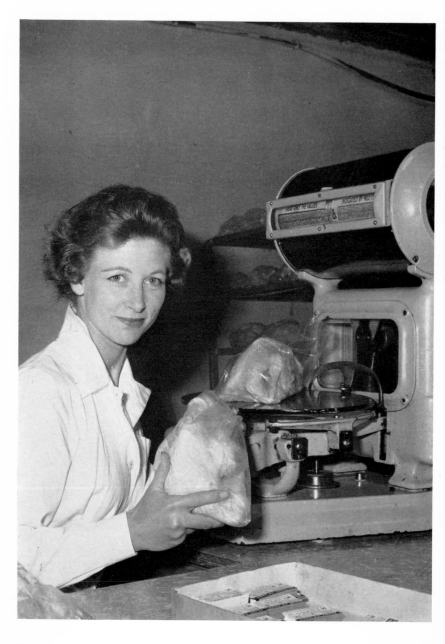

Plate 30 *The finished product of the broiler units is a clean, efficiently packed bird ready for the oven. The last stage before packing is weighing. (Photo S.A.I. Ltd.)*

fill the gap, and sometimes when this beef scarcity happens people will turn to pork for a change, but, whether it is in the production of pork or bacon, the pig occupies an important place in our farming economy.

Now, if the pig industry is specialized by production of large numbers in big units, the poultry industry can be said to be even more so. So much so, in fact, that some types of poultry production have been called 'factory farming', and indeed these intensive units do not need to be near a farm at all, as the stock are inside all the time and the feed is brought to them.

On many farms in Scotland the poultry were usually looked after by the farmer's wife or daughters and from the sale of the eggs or the roasting birds they got a lot of their housekeeping money. There are still farms where hens are kept for the supply of eggs and poultry meat for the farmer's family, but when it comes to the commercial production of poultry for eggs or meat the situation has changed dramatically from just a few years ago. On a very extensive sheep farm in the north of Scotland, say in Sutherland, where a good part of a big sheep-holding may be rocky mountains on which there is little vegetation at all, it may be possible to see an average of 10 acres of land to every sheep. But in the Lowlands it is possible to see on 10 acres an intensive poultry enterprise producing broiler chickens worth £400,000 a year. This is the type of fantastic contrast which can be found between modern farming and the more traditional types—although some people refuse to call these intensive poultry units farming at all.

The main methods of production are for eggs, in the battery system where the layers are in rows of cages set in tiers and all the feeding and cleaning are done automatically, and for poultry meat or broiler production where the chickens spend their short life in huge batches on a litter-floor hut where the lighting is artificial and again the feeding is automatic. In the case of the broiler huts, which will produce several crops of broilers a year, during the time between the departure of the old lot to the processing plant and the arrival of the young chicks the litter is completely cleared and the huts thoroughly fumigated and disinfected, as with such intensive stocking the disease risk increases.

The astronomical increase in the production of these small broiler chickens was made possible by the demand which they met from the public, who can buy a complete chicken ready for the oven or even already roasted for ten shillings, more or less, depending on the size of the chicken.

This demand arises from the fact that so many housewives work nowadays, so they want quickly produced meals, and this is one need the young broiler provides—but there are still some people who prefer to have their eggs from hens which are on free range in fields and their poultry meat from more mature chickens which, too, have lived outdoors or at least in less cramped production conditions.

But this is one of the many examples of how public taste may cause the food producer to change his methods—or on the other hand these new methods which created these millions of small chickens also created the public taste which led to the increased and increasing demand for them.

CHAPTER 16

AUTUMN HARVEST AND THE MOVEMENT OF STOCK

IN spite of the summer shows and other activities, the work of the farm must go on, and even before the show season has finished the fields of cereals will have been changing colour and the harvest approaching, or even begun and finished in the early districts. The fields of wheat and oats will have turned to varying shades of gold and the barley almost white.

We discussed corn-growing at sufficient length in Chapter 9 to have a fair appreciation of what is happening. The main cereal crop in Scotland is barley, and it is used for two purposes, feeding to stock or for brewing and distilling into beer or whisky.

Every year more and more of the corn crops are cut by the combine-harvesters which we have already mentioned. This system has replaced the older systems, first the sickle with which the corn was cut by hand, and later the binder, pulled by a horse and leaving the sheaves in rows to be set up later in stooks, and still later carted into the cornyard for storing in stacks or ricks until the threshing-machine came to the farm. The arrival of the threshing-machine was always a big event and especially exciting for the young people on the farm, because on so many farms colonies of rats live under the ricks and, as the last sheaves were being cleared from the foundations of the ricks, the small fry would be standing waiting, armed with sticks to be used in a rat hunt which was often wildly exciting and noisy. The cries of the children chasing the escaping rats rose above the loud hum of the threshing-machine as the sheaves were fed into it.

But with modern pest-control methods there are not so many rats on farms now and, of course, the combine does away with the need for a stackyard. Many farmers took great pride in their cornyards, in the regularity of the spacing and line of the stacks, and in the accurate building of the stacks, which were topped with rushes or straw to keep the rain out. A well-built stackyard made, and still makes, a fine sight on many farms.

Even the type of combine used in the modern harvest is changing. Many of the original ones cut the corn and filled it into sacks which were dropped off as they were filled and picked up and carted into the grain store later. But this system needed extra labour, so more and more of the combines of today are of the tanker type, which cuts out the hard work of handling sacks. In this system the combine cuts and threshes the corn, which is delivered into a tanker or truck travelling alongside the combine or into a tank on the combine itself.

Farmers who grow cereals on a large scale and use combines also need equipment for drying and storing the grain, because it is not being stored in stoocks or stacks as in the older system. Combined corn usually has more moisture than stacked corn, and in order to store it properly this moisture content must be reduced to about 16 per cent or less to be sure the corn will not become mouldy when stored in large quantities.

The barley is stored and during the winter can be ground into meal and mixed with other ingredients which the farmer can buy. These other ingredients will include maize, beans, cotton-cake or ground nut-cake, which are imported from abroad.

Some farmers like to do their own feed mixing, but many prefer to buy the highly concentrated feeds from manufacturers of feeding compounds, who are, of course, big customers for the barley which is the main element in many of these compound feeds. Some of these feeds are very highly specialized products and may contain trace elements, tiny proportions of chemicals which are vital for healthy stock.

Many years ago Scotland provided a striking example of these trace elements. Over a large area of the north of Scotland sheep pined away and sheep pine was a heavy drain on the flocks. Then it was discovered that over thousands of acres on which the sheep pastured there was a deficiency of a trace element in cobalt, a tiny, tiny trace element, but it was missing, and when it was replaced in the pastures the trouble was cleared.

Some of these compound feeds come in cubes or thin 'pencils' and they are easily handled and fed. They have a high proportion of valuable protein and starch and are generally known as concentrates, because they are very concentrated feed. The other feeds, like hay, silage, kale, and roots, are known as bulk feeds. Some dairy farmers use more concentrates than others, but these concentrates are expensive and their economic use has to be studied. The farmer must ensure that the stock are getting adequate food to enable them to produce their maximum, whether it be milk or beef or pork.

The modern methods of harvesting by tanker combines, drying plant, and storage buildings or silos are a big advance on the old methods we have described.

Among the other advantages of properly dried, cleaned, and stored grain is the fact that it can be kept and released on to the market when the farmer thinks fit, and so avoids harvest-time gluts which occurred at first when farmers had combines but few buildings for drying and storing, which meant that the grain had to go straight off the farm to the merchants who handled the corn. This often caused a drop in price at this time of the year. A drop in price does not mean that the farmer gets less, because, remember, when we explained the Price Review system we showed that the farmer gets a guaranteed price from the Government for his grain and if it falls below that the Government— which means the taxpayers—make up the difference. This is called a deficiency payment, as the Government make up the deficiency between the guaranteed price and the market price the grain makes when it is sold. But every effort is made to keep this deficiency payment as low as possible, so farmers are given incentives to spread the marketing of their grain over the year. This is done by giving a bonus to farmers who will enter contracts for forward delivery.

The combine-harvester represents one of the many great mechanical revolutions in farming practice, one of many profound changes which have come over the operations of British farmers and, looking back on these changes, it can be interesting trying to think what others the future may hold.

For instance, the aeroplane, the helicopter, and the hovercraft could take a bigger part in farming. The helicopter and the aeroplane already do, but not to anything like the extent they do in New Zealand, where huge regions have their fertilizers applied from the air.

The oxen gave way to the horse for ploughing the land and the horse gave way to the tractor, but the tractor has one or two disadvantages, and one is that it cannot go on to very wet land and cannot be used over and over, repeating operations on some types of land. So it would seem that there could be a place for the hovercraft. Already chemicals for protecting crops and killing weeds or fertilizers are applied from the air on many farms.

About this time of year farmers think of ways to help to 'shorten the winter' by extending the grazing season, so allowing stock to stay out of doors for longer and save the expense of preserving or buying in food for them. It is also beneficial for them to have some green succulent feed in the winter.

One of the best grazing countries in the world is New Zealand, where the climate is supposed to be somewhat similar to ours, but when people start making comparisons they forget that the climate in New Zealand is such that farmers can grow grass almost all the year round, whereas for several months of the year, even in the more favoured areas, we are unable to grow grass.

But there are some varieties of grass which will grow quite late in the autumn and earlier in the spring. So one of the jobs on the farm is sowing ryegrass or kale or rape on which the stock can graze in late autumn or early spring.

The late summer and early autumn are busy times for the livestock men. The draft ewes will be selected for the sales, where they will be bought by Lowland farmers to produce lambs on the lower ground. The producers of early fat lambs will want to have bought their ewes for the production of these lambs between July and September. Some of these ewes will have been mated already with the rams and the others will be mated straight away. These ewes will have a considerable amount of hand feeding during the winter and concentrates will be given them until the flush of spring grass comes.

Just as the first strawberries to appear on the shop counters make much higher prices than they do later in the season when they are not so scarce, so do these early lambs make much higher prices than the lambs which are born later on in much greater numbers. When the first of these early lambs appear in the marts there is keen competition between the butchers who will buy the lambs and soon have in their windows big bills announcing 'New Season's Lamb'.

But that is a market for lambs in early spring, so let us get back to the back end of the year again, a time when thousands of sheep change hands. This is the time of the year when the flockmasters have 'the harvest of the hills', when thousands and thousands of lambs come down from the hills to the big sales centres for disposal to the men who will feed and fatten them or buy some of them for breeding. More than 30,000 lambs could be sold in great sales centres like Lairg in Sutherland in one day, and similar huge sales, sometimes going on for several days, will be held in other Highland centres or in the great sheep markets of the Borders.

Before the lambs can be sold they must be collected and sorted and treated. On the hills these 'gatherings' as they are called are busy times for the shepherds and their dogs, who may cover many miles collecting the sheep off their hirsels. The lambs are collected in huge sets of pens on the farms called fanks, and the males and the females are separated along with the best, the not so good, and the poor lots. The best lots of lambs are called the top draws and they go to market first, then come the second draws and the shotts or poor lambs.

The flocks of breeding ewes will again be injected against disease and the time at which the ram is put among the ewes will depend on the time the farmer wants the lambs to arrive in the spring. In hill flocks the rams will be put out among the ewes in November, early or later. Certainly later in the colder north hills than in the southern uplands, where the spring and the grass come that little bit earlier. The lambing, in fact, 'creeps' northward as the spring comes over the land.

For a few weeks before turning the rams to the ewes the ewes will be well fed, a system known as 'flushing', and the aim is to ensure a good lamb crop.

The calves and store cattle will also be coming down off the hills to be big sales centres to be disposed of to the men who feed them to produce the good beef.

We have already seen that efforts have been made to achieve direct sales from some areas, particularly the islands, through group or co-operative effort to get better prices. At one Border centre as many as 8,000 suckled calves will be sold in three days and many of them will go over the Border to England to farmers who have plenty of grass. In the same way thousands of lambs will be bought for feeding and fattening south of the Border.

It will be seen that in a year where the weather has been bad and the grass has not come away very well there will be a lessening of demand for these lambs and calves and the prices will drop, a serious business for the store stock producers, as there are no guaranteed prices for store stock.

If the farmers in the feeding areas have good grass and are doing well, then the benefit will come to the men who produce the store stock—just another indication of how experiences in one area will affect the economics of another.

It is the aim of the store lamb and calf men to produce a high quality article to satisfy the needs of the buyers and these buyers will come back to the same centre year after year and buy the same kind of stock when they know that it is good. Most of these buyers like to buy their calves in fairly large lots and if one man needs sixty he will buy three lots of twenty and the sale is over for him. They do not like to buy calves in ones or twos, for the time is eaten up in looking at and bidding for them and, what is even worse, the calves will not be so level in size and quality.

So if there are many small-scale farmers, like Highland crofters, who may have only one or two calves each, they are urged to make up larger lots of an even size and quality by combining. This is not easy, as so many of these small farmers are individualistic and like to see their calves sold on their own —which often means a poorer price.

The calves must be well fed and cared for, as they may have a long journey to the sale and another long journey after it. If the calf is not well managed in this way, it will not do so well when it arrives at its new home, and this will be noticed by the buyer, who will watch out for calves from this farmer next time.

So the grain, the lambs, and the calves will be collected and disposed of in the various ways. Another big back-end job is the potato harvest. Like other jobs on the farm, this provides casual work for workers' families or people from near-by towns who will come out to the fields for the work and the cash.

As we have already mentioned, Scotland has a very big trade with England for seed potatoes, so the potatoes will be lifted— usually by different kinds of mechanical diggers and gathered by the casual workers—and stored in great straw-lined clamps of earth or in special buildings which will keep the frost off them. When the times comes for the potatoes to be sold, for seed or for human food—these are called the ware potatoes—they are, put over a machine which 'dresses' them, sorting out the large, the smaller seed size, and the very small, which are often fed to stock.

This machine which runs the potatoes over different kinds of riddles which select the different sizes can also help to regulate the market. The Potato Marketing Board may stipulate the minimum size of potato which will be kept and say that the potatoes will be dressed to a certain riddle size.

The main method of disposing of the seed potatoes is by selling them to a merchant who will find a market for them in England, usually through another merchant. These seed potatoes are very strictly graded and great care is taken to ensure they are disease-free and the right size for the job.

Here, too, there are some excellent examples of group or co-operative effort. For instance, say a Lincolnshire farmer gets a consignment of seed potatoes which may have been damaged in transit or not very carefully dressed, he may be unable to complain to the farmer who grew them, as these potatoes were mixed in with lots from other farmers. But a group of farmers in eastern Ross joined to produce a high-quality, 'well-dressed' variety of seed, and they did more than that. Each bag was sealed and labelled with the farm of origin, so the grower could be easily identified.

Buchan Meat Producers, the multi-million-pound meat co-operative we have already mentioned, have also started a big department handling potatoes for their members and seeking export outlets in overseas countries.

Soon now the richly coloured autumn leaves will be falling, the countryside and the woodlands will begin to look bare, and there may come a hint of frost, and winter is on the doorstep.

CHAPTER 17

WINTER AND MARKETING PROBLEMS

WHILE there may be periods of the year when there is a little less activity than at others, things are always going on in farming, and even before one activity or operation draws to an end some other enterprise is taking shape or some other essential operation has been set in motion and a cycle starts again.

Before the winter finally arrives farmers who intend spreading basic slag or lime will try to get as much of this work done as possible while the land is still dry. If the ground is wet, the wheels of tractors and lorries doing the spreading can cause a considerable amount of damage on good grassland.

As the days shorten the land changes colour to browns and shades of red as the pastures or stubbles are turned over by the ploughs, so that by the time the New Year arrives a great acreage of the fields show us the freshly turned earth.

About this time the opportunity will also be taken to clean out some of the ditches on the farm, so that the field drains can work properly. Well-drained land is the best land and it is no good hoping to see early grass or any other good crops on land that is not free draining. In the first chapter we discussed how man had given the land its 'complexion', and one of the most profound changes in this complexion was brought about by draining. The Romans often built their roads along ridges of land or low hills, because so much of the flat or valley land was undrained bog. If you stood on high ground and looked on a flat strath as it could be many years ago, before it was drained, you could hardly imagine the contrast. The great land improvers not only drained the land but removed stones and boulders, cleared the vast regions of degenerate scrubland, and laid out the fields in their regular or irregular patterns of squares or triangles or many-sided figures.

If your eyes could X-ray a field, they would see under the surface long grids or lines like the veins of a leaf, one drain leading into another and the bigger leading into a main and eventually into a ditch, or a burn or a river. It was these vast schemes of drainage, carried out before the days of tractors or earth-moving equipment, which changed the face of the countryside and laid the foundations for the production of the crops and the stock from these fields.

It will be too early in the year to cut hedges for laying them, because the sap will not as yet have dried back, but in the autumn, hedges which do not need to be laid can be trimmed.

The cattle will have started their winter-feeding programme in good time, for it is important not to be late in starting this if production is to be maintained. At this time of the year, too, animals show shaggier coats to protect them from the cold, and many breeds look different from their appearance in high summer, when they might have appeared at a show in their sleek summer coats.

The stock will be fed bulk feed and concentrates and the concentrates are very important for the dairy cattle. With an adequate amount of bulk feed of good quality a cow should be able to maintain herself in good condition in the winter and give perhaps a gallon of milk a day. If she is giving more milk, she will require some concentrates, which will be fed at the rate of about three pounds by weight for every gallon of milk. In order to economize on concentrates as far as possible, most farmers will make sure that they give preference to the needs of the newly calved cows, which will be given more milk than those which have been milking for some time, cows whose output will be going down and which may be going dry in readiness to calve again.

This question of winter milk production is another interesting example of financial considerations exerting a great influence on what farmers do.

We have seen that before the creation of the Milk Marketing Boards most of the milk was produced off the grass in the summer, and we had oversupply of the market at one period and undersupply in another. Surplus milk was made into butter and cheese, but there was not a great deal of order in the marketing of the milk.

The Boards did a great deal of good work, and two of the main things they did were to encourage the people to drink more milk and therefore buy more liquid milk. Thus a far better price was paid than for the surplus milk which went for manufacturing. The Boards also encouraged a more even production of milk between summer and winter, but we shall come to this in a moment.

Butter and cheese were also being imported from New Zealand, Holland, Denmark, and Canada. The population was increasing and more milk was going into the big towns and more of the butter and cheese was being made in the big creameries and not so much on the farms. But there are still a number of farm cheese-makers in Scotland.

When the Second World War came the nation paid a dear price for neglecting its agricultural industry for so long. Imports of everything, especially food, had to be kept down to a minimum and there was a great drive to improve the production of food from our own fields and hills.

The shortage of milk had been most felt in the winter, as this was not the traditional time for its production. It became necessary so to arrange the price paid to the farmer that he would be encouraged to produce more in winter and a little less in summer. Before the market was organized by the Boards it was a free-for-all, but the Boards made possible a seasonal scale of milk prices with encouragement for winter milk by means of a higher price than that paid for summer milk. Of course, farms could not change their calving plans overnight, but gradually the situation improved and more milk was forthcoming from farms which were encouraged to go in for dairying.

After the war imports of butter were resumed and so a problem arose of the manufacture of butter from our surplus milk. We have already shown that liquid milk made a far better price than the surplus sent to be made into butter and cheese or powdered milk, and some means had to be found of keeping up milk supplies without producing too much surplus for manufacture. The result was the pool price already referred to in a former chapter. It simply meant that the liquid-milk price and the manufacturing prices were pooled and this pooled price paid to the farmer. Let us say the liquid price was 3s. 6d. per gallon and the manufacturing price was 1s. 6d., the total income from the milk at these prices was pooled and this total averaged over the whole supply, so that the pool price would be lower than the guaranteed price paid for the quantity which was needed for the liquid market.

This quantity of milk needed for the liquid market is estimated by the Government, in consultation with the Farmers' Unions, and it gets the full guaranteed price. It is called the standard quantity. Now, if production goes away above this standard quantity and a big proportion of the milk has to be sent for manufacture, it is obvious that the greater number of gallons paid for at the lower price will bring down the pool price, so this system acts as a brake on overproduction.

There is another element in the price of milk and this is the payment for quality. Here, too, it is on a sliding scale, based on the butterfat content of the milk and on the content of its other solids which are called the non-fatty solids, but which along with the butterfat are a measurement of the quality of the milk.

Dairy farmers have a particular complaint against the Government and that is that theirs is the only product where the retail price of the milk sold in the shops is still decided by and controlled by the Government. When, in order to see fair shares for all, food rationing and controlled prices were brought in during the war years, the Government promised the Milk Marketing Boards that when the war finished the Boards would get back their full marketing powers, including decisions on the price. But milk is the one single commodity produced by British farmers where the retail price is still fixed by the Government, which so far have not seen fit to give the Boards their full powers back.

Because the price of milk has been kept at what many farmers think is an uneconomically low figure as far as they as producers are concerned, milk production on many farms became less profitable or produced no profits at all.

This resulted in many farmers going out of milk production,

in very large numbers, every year, with the result that there are fears that a situation may arise where there is not enough milk produced in Britain for the liquid market, and leaders in the dairy industry fear that if this steady departure of producers should coincide with a season or a year of very bad weather which reduced the output and quality of grass and the grains used in the feeds it could be serious. So when Price Review time comes round the Government is urged to pay a higher price to the producers in order to keep them in milk production. Apart from some very small dairy farms which did not have a very big milk enterprise, the decision to leave milk production could not have been an easy one for many of these dairy farmers, as the production of milk demands some quite expensive equipment, for milking the cows, handling the milk and sterilizing the equipment.

This applies to some other branches of farming where expensive machinery is used in the operations, so it is not so easy for some farmers to switch from one type of production to another. Most farms are run on intensive or semi-intensive lines, with high-yielding fields resulting from intensive use of fertilizers, or animals fed on expensive concentrates to increase their yields. When things get difficult some farmers speak of turning over to extensive types of farming, sometimes called 'dog-and-stick' farming, which is just what it implies. The whole farm is put down to grass and a breeding herd or flock is kept for store stock production with the young stock sold off as soon as possible and all the farmer needs to look after the stock are a dog and a stick.

But dog and stick, or extensive, farming systems would not work on many farms, especially good arable Lowland farms, for these farms may have been bought at a high price, perhaps £200 per acre, or, if they are tenanted, the rent may be quite high. As dog-and-stick farming tends to produce low returns per acre, this type of farming could not produce enough return to pay the rent or the interest on the money which so many farmers have to borrow to buy their farms. So farmers who find one branch of farming not paying well, or not paying at all, have a difficult job deciding what to turn to.

In recent years many have turned to cereals, chiefly barley, as a cash crop, but here the production soared and in a few years the tonnage of barley produced in Britain began to create problems of finding a market for it, and farmers began to be warned about the risk of overproduction.

Apart from the ploughing and the tending of the stock, there is plenty of other work to be done. There is so much machinery about a modern farm these days that the bigger farms have their own machinery housed in special, big sheds with storage for spare parts and workbenches for repair and other work. The winter is a good time to do this, so that when the time comes for the machines to be used no precious time will be lost because they are not in working order.

For the farmers who fatten stock there is another winter interest, the fatstock shows and special sales. A Christmas fatstock show and special sale at a local mart is a big event with keen competition between the fine, beautifully finished animals.

A championship at these Christmas shows usually adds a lot to the price of the animal, and the butcher who buys it will display the cards or rosettes in his window when the time comes to sell the meat from the animals.

The shows and sales are more than just places to show and sell animals. Here farmers meet other farmers and discuss their problems and how things are going on other farms.

Apart from the local shows, there are the national ones. The Scottish National Fatstock Show is held in Edinburgh about the end of November and some of the best fatstock, cattle, sheep, and pigs, and seeds and potatoes are on show. It is quite likely that the champion animals from many of the breeds or crosses will go on to the Royal Smithfield Show in London, to meet the champions from English and Welsh shows, and often the Scottish champion has repeated its success at the big show in London.

The London show is also a big show of machinery by manufacturers, and it is very popular with farmers from all over Britain, those who are interested in stock and those who want to see the latest machines—or both. Another reason for the popularity of the Royal Smithfield Show is that it is held at a time of year when there is not a great deal doing on the farm—in the first week in December—and not only the farmers but often their wives and families go with them and do shopping or see some of the theatres.

The big dairy shows are also a winter attraction, the London show being in October.

It is a treat for the country people just to go to the town, as it is for townspeople to go to the country.

These big national shows, apart from the great displays of machinery and stock, have an educational aspect, and during the week there will be many demonstrations of new feeding systems, carcass-production displays, and many other events of an instructive nature for farmers.

There is one section of the Royal Smithfield Show of great interest to another section of Scottish farming, the seed-potato producers. On one of the floors of the huge hall at Earl's Court, the potato-seed merchants have their stalls and meet many of their customers from the potato-growing areas of England.

CHAPTER 18

RURAL LIFE, EDUCATION, AND RESEARCH

WE have considered sufficient in the pages of this book to know that farming is an important business, vital to the well-being of the nation, about which there is a great deal to be learned. In its basic principles it has remained almost the same since time began, although, of course, the pattern has been constantly changing.

At one time a man who rented land from a landowner would pay for it by giving the owner of the land an agreed amount of wool, butter, lambs, or corn, or a period of service. When trade with foreign countries began the landlord wanted to buy some of the things which were being imported, and so he asked for rent in money instead of produce. The workers would also want monetary payment and even the farmers themselves found that they could now buy some of the things which they had previously either produced themselves or had had to do without altogether.

Before the Industrial Revolution began the farm was the centre of the community life in the countryside. Cottagers, or cottars as they are called in Scotland (remember Robert Burns's 'The Cottar's Saturday Night'?), or their families would help with the seasonal work on the farms and, in return, might get a row of potatoes in a field or a load of farmyard manure for their own small plot of land. Some small farmers who had no horse or their own would also help on a bigger farm or estate and in return the farmer would provide the horse to help them with their own hay crops. Indeed, the whole emphasis of this old way of life was on help and co-operation, and we have shown especially how this was done on the hill-sheep farms by 'neighbouring'.

There were no mowing-machines or reapers or binders. All the hay and corn had to be cut by hand by gangs of men using scythes. When it was ready to be carted it had to be pitched by hand on to the carts. The co-operation of the workers on the farms in these old days proved the truth of the proverb that 'Many hands make light work', and this was, in fact, the only way to get all the seasonal work done.

Even today, when potato-lifting time comes, it is the families from the farm cottages or from the near-by towns or villages who come to do the lifting after the potatoes have been dug up by machines—although we have shown that there are machines which lift and load potatoes, too.

The large gatherings of people at these big seasonal tasks brought them together in a social as well as in a working capacity. The womenfolk would carry food and drink out to the fields, and when the harvest was all in—in some parts of Scotland the last sheaf was called the 'clyack' sheaf—there was the harvest-home celebration in the main barn in the farm or the village hall and a harvest-home service in the church, which would be decorated with sheaves and autumn flowers.

Old people look back with nostalgia to the great happiness of these occasions, for these were the days when the country people made their own enjoyment before the days of the cinema, music hall—which were perhaps far away in a town anyway when they did come—or the radio or the television.

The coming of the Industrial Revolution brought big changes. It took many people off the land, but it also gave a great impetus to home food production from our own fields to feed the increasing thousands and thousands in the factories. Such was the demand for food for the industrial workers that an historic change took place in British Government policy. This was the repeal of the Corn Laws to allow cheaper food to come in from overseas, a policy which, apart from the two great wars, did great damage to British farming. Only in the two wars, when it was difficult to bring food in from abroad because of enemy action, did British farming achieve anything of the prosperity it had in its 'golden age' in the early eighteenth century.

Apart from the workers, many small farmers left the land and many of the small farms were amalgamated or joined to bigger farms, and this trend continues; in fact, it is actively encouraged by the Government, which wants to see bigger farming units, farms big enough to provide a full-time job for a farmer or his family.

It is still possible for workers to leave the land in steady numbers, as the bigger farms are increasing the use of machinery to replace the workers. This increasing use of machinery has resulted in the fact that farm workers need to be highly skilled in many crafts, and not just in handling machinery, but in knowing basic facts about the nutrition of stock, the fertilization and protection of crops and so on. On many farms the farm worker is as far away in ability and skill from the farm labourer of old as the combine harvester is from the man with the scythe.

In spite of all this modernization, however, there is still a feeling of togetherness among farmers, and a sense of belonging on the land. There is a great freemasonry among farmers, for they are never short of subjects to talk about and they are talking about living things, plants and stock, and the many systems and operations they use on their farms.

There is still a community spirit and we can see it in the different kinds of groupings and co-operatives in which farmers join for mutual help, sometimes in quite small ways and sometimes in huge business concerns, like one co-operative which covers northern England and southern Scotland which has an annual turnover of away above £25,000,000.

There are farmers in groups, as we have shown, for keeping a supply of calves or pigs for fattening, for buying their seeds, fertilizers, and equipment, and for selling their stock and their corn. But the corn merchant still has his place in the countryside, and still provides a varied and very personal service to the farmer, often being an adviser on many things apart from knowing the farmer on a purely business level.

While there are big farms run like big businesses and big units for the production of chickens and eggs with millions of birds in them, farming is still largely an individual way of life and work, for the workers as well as for the farmers, and between the farmers and their workers there is a special understanding or mutual goodwill which exists in few other industries. A farm worker may spend the day in a field out of sight of the farm, and the farmer will know that the job is being done as skilfully and as fast as possible, whereas in a factory there are overseers and others whose job it is to see that the work is done properly and quickly.

This is a very special relationship and it could arise that the farmer and the worker have a common love of the land and the work that goes on it. They see the seed planted and harvested, struggle with it in bad harvests, or with the sheep in the hills when the blizzards come. They see animals born and die and the seasons come and go in the same succession, but seldom in the same pattern. The farmer and his men have more discussions about what may be happening than a mere giving and receiving of orders. Their knowledge of the land is really intimate, for even the fields have their own names. A chapter could be written on this alone, for these field names arise from an amazing variety of causes—it may have been from a character who lived there long ago, from the nearness of a building or landmark, from the shape, height or size or aspect, or from a hundred and one other things that resulted in a field having a name rather than a number on an ordnance map.

For all his great importance to the nation the farm worker receives a wage that is in most comparisons lower than the wages obtained by workers in many other industries in the cities and towns. The workers, like the farmers, have their own organization to work on their behalf and look after their interests, negotiating wage claims, adjusting hours and deciding how long holidays they should be allowed or how much they should get if they should have to work extra time, or overtime as it is called. The workers' hours and wages are decided by the Scottish Agricultural Wages Board, on which employers and workers are represented along with one or two people appointed by the Government who are independent of either side of the industry.

The average farm is a small unit, so there is no great collection of workers under one employer as in a factory. Even on the very big farms the work can be done with machines and between ten or twenty workers, with casual help at peak times. It is perhaps this smallness of the average enterprise which brings this intimacy of relationship between the worker and his employer in farming that has resulted in the absence of strikes in the agricultural industry. Also absent are disputes about demarcation. In a big shipyard there may be a strike because one set of workers say they should do a certain job while others claim they should do it. But the farm worker may be skilled in more than one craft and he will turn his hands to these crafts as his skills are needed. Of course, on the biggest farms there will be specialist workers who are confined to their speciality because the enterprise is big enough to keep them busy all the year round in one task. But in the main, even the specialists may turn their hands to some other job in a season of peak demand for labour.

While there may be some dispute of the real value of some of them, farm workers have certain perquisites in addition to or in lieu of their pay, such as free milk and potatoes and a cottage at a nominal rent, or a piece of land of their own for growing vegetables.

For instance, a farmer may build some quite nice cottages or small bungalows for his workers, but by law he can get only a few shillings a week against the workers' pay for these houses. This means, of course, that the house goes with the job and it is known as a 'tied house', but this is known in many industries and even professions. In banking, for instance, in many country towns the bank manager lives in the house that is part of the bank, or of which the bank is part and when he leaves his job he leaves the house. It could be said that No. 10 Downing Street is a tied house, as when the Prime Minister ceases to be Prime Minister he has to leave that house!

While the tied-house system has its drawbacks and its critics, it generally works fairly well. Of course, the farm worker has one advantage over the townsman. He has no fares to pay to and from his work, as he lives on the job. And a careful farm worker can enjoy a fairly good life. There is one farm in Aberdeenshire where about ten of the workers have their own cars—and they have no problems of parking or keeping them at home.

One big change has come over the farm worker, apart from

the huge addition to his skill and knowledge, and that is the method of engaging him or hiring him. This used to be done at local hiring fairs, or feeing markets, as they were called in some parts. At this market the farmers and workers mingled and a farmer who had lost a worker for one reason or another would talk to one or two likely men and 'fee' one for the year, and often their wages were paid in a lump sum at the end of six months or even longer.

The back end of the year was the traditional time when workers changed jobs if they wished, and even now that workers are engaged on the same basis as any other worker and are paid weekly it is still a traditional time for changing jobs, although the advertising columns of the Press now have announcements of vacancies or jobs wanted all the year round.

We have made clear that the modern farm worker is a skilled and knowledgeable technician and as the demands for increased skill increase so has there been an extension of the facilities for training workers. In the old days a worker was taken on as a lad and he learned as he grew up, and on many farms this is still done. But today there are many facilities for training in apprenticeship schemes and day-release courses or block-release courses. These three explain themselves. Under the apprenticeship scheme a boy is taken on as an apprentice and is allowed off on special days to go to a near-by school or institute for specialized instruction, or he may get off for a block period or several weeks to get this instruction.

The next stage above this for workers, or for farmers' sons or others who may want to be farmers or farm managers, is a diploma which can be got after a three-year course at an agricultural college or a degree in agricultural science at one of the universities.

The day has gone when it was thought that a boy who was not very bright could always get a job on a farm. To do the job properly a farm worker, as we have said, must be skilled in many operations, often handling costly machinery, or engaging in tasks which call for precision in execution.

It is amazing how many townspeople have an interest in farming and, especially in Scotland, there is a very large percentage of the population who are only one or two generations removed from the land and this applies to some of our greatest doctors, lawyers, and other professional men.

In the terrible depression days for British agriculture in the 1930s there was a great drift from the land of farmers' sons and of workers. The workers went to jobs in the towns, or on the dole, and the farmers' sons, finding no future in a depressed industry like farming, took up banking, medicine or some other profession.

That has changed today and many a farmer holds his degree in agricultural science. Not everybody who has a diploma or degree can afford to buy a farm, for the price of good land is very high. But there are many other branches of the industry or its allied industries where a young man with a love of the land can still be linked with the land professionally.

We have shown that farming is a science-based industry and the industry uses hundreds of scientists—in the laboratories of the research institutions which serve it or in the advisory services which pass on to the farmer the results of the research done by the scientists in these laboratories.

Scotland is very rich in its agricultural research institutions and a brief mention of the main ones demonstrates this. In the north-east at Aberdeen are two famous centres of research—the Rowett Research Institute, which has specialized in animal nutrition and allied disciplines (it was here that the barley-beef system was brought to practical operation), and the Macaulay Institute of Soil Research.

Near Dundee the sister industry of horticulture has its research station at Mylnefield and, in the west, in the main dairying area, is the Hannah Institute for Dairy Research. In and around Edinburgh is a cluster of research centres. These include the stations or institutes of the Society for Research in Plant Breeding; Animal Diseases Research Association; the Animal Breeding Research Organization; the Institute of Animal Genetics; the Poultry Research Centre, and the Scottish Station of the National Institution for Agricultural Engineering. There is also the Hill Farming Research Organization, which has experimental farms in three different areas of Scotland where the farms reflect the different environmental conditions of these areas. Also in Edinburgh is the Scientific Services Station of the Department of Agriculture for Scotland.

That is an impressive outline of some of the institutes pursuing research for farming, but it must be made clear that while these stations are based in Scotland they are of United Kingdom or international importance, for science knows no boundaries and an expert on, say, the nutrition of the dairy cow who is working at the Hannah in Ayrshire may be found visiting America or Russia, seeing what scientists there are doing in this kind of research.

We have indicated that there are advisory services which pass to the farmer, or interpret for him, the results and benefits of the research carried out by these scientists. This is a very important aspect of modern farming—getting across to the man in the field the results of the work of the scientist in the laboratory.

This is done by the advisory services, and they are administered by the three Scottish agricultural colleges. In each county there are one or more advisory officers plus certain specialists. For instance, in a county like Aberdeen, which has, in addition to general farming, a considerable interest in dairying and poultry, the local advisory staff will also have specialists in dairying and poultry. Behind these advisory officers in the field there will be, at the college headquarters or in the college regional offices, other specialists, veterinary investigation officers, chemists, botanists, economists, plant pathologists, and so on, so that the country is covered by a network of scientifically trained people on whom the farmer may call for advice on any scientific or practical aspect of farming, from the keeping of his books and records to the feeding of his dairy cows.

But this is not the only advisory service available to the farmer. Many of the big firms who sell fertilizers, seeds, feeding-stuffs, and so on to the farmer have their own advisory staffs, again science graduates, who are available to give the farmer skilled advice on anything from feeds and fertilizers to seeds and machinery.

These scientific advisers call on the farm at the invitation of the farmer or sometimes they hold conferences on specialized subjects. These conferences may range from two whole days with several expert speakers on beef production to an evening meeting in one small area with one speaker on one subject.

But all the time they are spreading the news of the progress in all the sciences on which modern agriculture is based and in this and in many other ways our farmers are improving their production and their skills.

So we come to the end of a look at what is happening on the farms in Scotland and what is behind what is happening on the farms in Scotland. It may not have been a very deep look, but maybe it will give a little better understanding of the farming pattern. We have seen something of how that pattern has evolved and how it is still changing and we have seen that the future will undoubtedly bring further changes, even faster and more profound than some of those we have mentioned or outlined.

Yet whatever changes there may be one thing is certain, and we have it in the promise which God made to Noah after the Flood and which is written in the Eighth Chapter of Genesis:

'While the earth remaineth, seed-time and harvest, and cold and heat, and summer and winter, and day and night shall not cease.'

INDEX

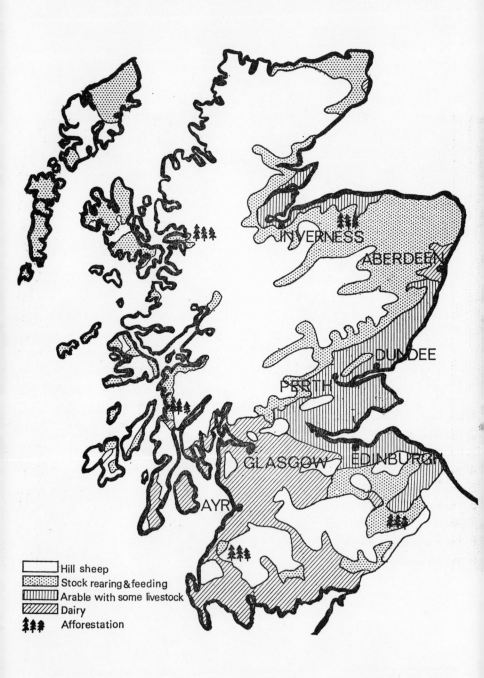

▢▢	Hill sheep
▨▨	Stock rearing & feeding
⊞⊞	Arable with some livestock
⧄⧄	Dairy
🌲🌲 🌲🌲	Afforestation

INVERNESS

ABERDEEN

DUNDEE

PERTH

GLASGOW   EDINBURGH

AYR